PRACTICING THE WRITING PROCESS 1

THE PARAGRAPH

BY
SHEILA C. CROWELL
&
ELLEN D. KOLBA

EDUCATIONAL DESIGN, INC.   **EDI 328**

Table of Contents

Introduction

For a long time, there has been a big difference between the way real writers—people who write for a living—write and the way students are taught to write in school. Real writers know a lot of things you may never have been told before:

- Sometimes you don't know what you really want to write about until you start writing.

- Thinking is part of writing.

- Putting words down on paper—any words—helps get your ideas flowing.

- It's all right to change your mind while you're writing—and to change what you've written.

- There are all kinds of special tricks you can use to make the job of writing easier.

This book will take you step by step through the process of writing the way a real writer does.

- It will help you get started.

- It will show you how to turn your ideas into sentences and paragraphs.

- It will give you practice in improving what you've written.

- If you have a computer with a word-processing program, it will help you make the most of it.

Most of all, it will teach you a method you will always be able to use . . . because anyone who can think can write.

PREWRITING

The first step in the writing process isn't the actual writing at all. It's a step called prewriting.

Prewriting is pre-writing. It is what you do before (pre-) you begin writing. It includes everything that you do to get started. Even some things you might not have thought of as writing can be part of prewriting.

- Thinking can be prewriting.

- Doodling can be prewriting.

- Making lists can be prewriting.

- Asking questions can be prewriting.

When you finish prewriting, you will have a clear idea of what you want to write about, and you will even have some of the writing done.

This section will start you on writing a descriptive paragraph. Each lesson begins with a warmup that gives you practice with some of the real writers' tricks and techniques. Then you will see how another student uses those techniques to work on a descriptive paragraph. Finally, you'll have a chance to start writing your own paragraph.

Getting Ideas

*The writing process begins when you think about
what you want to write.*

WARMUP

Writers write best when they write about what they know. Which of the following do you know something about? Underline the topics you know the most about.

cars   getting around the city
baby sitting   making money after school
basketball   George Washington
a rock group   computer games
American history   traveling
jobs   birds
music video

Try It

Look at the topics you've underlined. Then pick the one you're most interested in and write it here.

_____

Now write some of the things you know about the topic you have underlined. The box on the left shows what Todd knew about the topic "cars."

CARS   YOUR SUBJECT: _____

racing   _____

campers   _____

specially equipped—like
James Bond's   _____

designing your own   _____

demolition derby   _____

car repair and maintenance   _____

Sometimes you are asked to write about something you think you know nothing about—or maybe it's something you don't really want to write about. What's your reaction?

Marisa feels panicky. She's decided to write something about American history. All of a sudden, everything she's ever read about American history disappears from her head. Then she looks at the list again. George Washington is there. She knows something about him. In fact, when she starts to write down what she knows, she finds out that she knows more than she thought. Here is Marisa's list.

GEORGE WASHINGTON
first president
American Revolution
lived at Mt. Vernon
class trip to Mt. Vernon last year
he couldn't tell a lie—story about cutting down a cherry tree

---

Try It

Go back to the list at the beginning of the chapter. Find the topic that you think you know the *least* about. Look for one part of the topic that you *do* know something about. Then see if you can write three to five things about it.

SUBJECT: _____

_____

_____

_____

_____

Ronald has to write something about birds. All he knows at the start is that he doesn't like the topic very much. When his teacher says, "You can write about what you don't like as well as what you like," he breathes a sigh of relief.

Here is Ronald's list. Notice that he started with two things he doesn't like—noise and dirt—and then thought of some things about birds that aren't so bad.

BIRDS
noisy
pigeons are dirty
gray or brown
people like to feed the birds—old people in the park
feeding leftover bread to ducks and geese

Try It

Look at the list that begins the chapter again. Cross out the two topics you have already written something about. Now pick the last item in the first column and the first item in the second column to write about. Write your two subjects here. Then add three to five things you know about each one.

SUBJECT: _____   SUBJECT: _____

_____   _____

_____   _____

_____   _____

_____   _____

PRACTICING THE PROCESS

Lee's Paragraph

Lee's teacher, Ms. Daniels, has asked everyone in the class to write a one-paragraph essay. She reminds them that a paragraph

- has one main idea
- has about four to six sentences
- can describe something or tell a story

Each student may choose to describe a person or animal, a place, a thing, or an event. The first step for Lee is to decide what he wants to write about.

Lee makes four columns on a sheet of paper. He thinks and doodles for a few minutes and then writes.

PERSON/ANIMAL	PLACE	THING	EVENT
me	weird places	knives	weekends
friends	gym	shoes	game
snakes	zoo	traps	going to school

Your Paragraph WP   This symbol is for Word Processor users. If you have a Word Processor, use it for this activity and save the file.

Write three or four things in each column. They can be words, groups of words, or sentences. Don't worry about the order in which you write things. Don't worry about spelling or capitalization. The important thing is to just keep writing until you get a good idea.

PERSON/ANIMAL	PLACE	THING	EVENT
_____	_____	_____	_____
_____	_____	_____	_____
_____	_____	_____	_____

Lee's Paragraph

Lee keeps getting more ideas for his last column. He is starting to think about days when annoying things happened. This is what he adds to the last column:

getting up
oversleeping
furnace broken
losing lunch
money

Your Paragraph WP

Here are some more lines for each column. Look at what you've already written and pick the column that interests you the most. Then add as many ideas as you wish to that column.

_____ _____ _____ _____

_____ _____ _____ _____

_____ _____ _____ _____

_____ _____ _____

Lee's Paragraph

Now Lee knows that he wants to write about the kind of day when everything seems to go wrong, like the day that the alarm didn't go off and his whole family was late for work and school. He really wants everyone to know just how bad a day like that can be.

Your Paragraph WP

Look at what you added to your list. Were you thinking of any particular person, animal, place, thing, or event? Did you find something that you really want to write about? If not, start another list on a separate sheet of paper until you come to one category that makes you want to write more. When you have a general idea of what you want to write about, put it here.

I WANT TO WRITE ABOUT _____

Focusing

Focusing helps you keep your eye on what you want to write about.

WARMUP

In the last chapter, you chose a topic to write about. Your next step will be to decide what you want to say about the topic you have chosen. To do that, you will first list all the things you think you might want to include. Then you'll look over your list and decide what things in it you want to focus on, or concentrate on. Here are two activities that will help you understand what focusing is and why it is important.

Try It

A. Study the words below for 30 seconds. (Your teacher will tell you when to start and stop.) Look for all the words that name colors.

yellow	house	dog	bread
potato	red	barn	bird
cat	green	elephant	church
office	horse	purple	cheese
brown	egg	pickle	cottage
cabbage	rabbit	prison	gray

Now, COVER THE LIST OF WORDS and write down as many words as you can that name colors.

_____   _____

_____   _____

_____   _____

When you've finished, KEEP THE LIST OF WORDS COVERED. This time, write down as many words as you can that name foods.

_____   _____

_____   _____

_____   _____

UNCOVER THE WORDS. Compare the two lists that you wrote. Did you remember more color words than food words? Because you were focusing on color words, they stood out, and you were able to ignore the other words.

Try It

B. Try focusing again. Study the picture below, paying special attention to the objects that are circular in shape.

Now COVER THE PICTURE. Write down as many things as you can that are shaped like circles.

_____   _____   _____   _____

_____   _____   _____   _____

_____   _____   _____   _____

When you've finished, KEEP THE PICTURE COVERED. This time, write down as many things as you can that are shaped like triangles.

_____   _____   _____   _____

_____   _____   _____   _____

_____   _____   _____   _____

Compare your two lists. Did you find, again, that you noticed more when you were focused on a particular shape? When you knew what you were looking for, you were able to overlook all the objects without that shape. Focusing in this way will help you pick out what you need for your paragraph.

PRACTICING THE PROCESS

Lee's Paragraph

Lee has decided to write about all the things that can happen to ruin the day. He starts to make a list of the things he wants to include, writing them down as he thinks of them—in no particular order.

Here's what Lee writes.

> no heat
> alarm doesn't ring
> no clean shirts
> lose my lunch money
> have a fight with Dawn
> get a D on my test
> can't find my homework
> mother on my case

Your Paragraph WP

Make a list of the things you want to include in a paragraph about the topic you chose in the last lesson.

_____

_____

_____

_____

_____

Lee's Paragraph

When Lee looks at his list again, he realizes that he has too much for one paragraph. He has been putting down things that happened to him on a number of different days. He decides to focus on just one day.

Here are the changes Lee makes in his list.

> no heat
> alarm didn't ring
> ~~no clean shirts~~
> ~~lost my lunch money~~
> ~~had a fight with Dawn~~
> got a D on my test
> ~~couldn't find my homework~~
> mother on my case

Your Paragraph WP

Look at your list. Does everything on it describe just one person or one place or one thing? Take some time to think about it. What do you want to focus on? Cross out or put a mark next to all the details that have nothing to do with what you have decided to focus on.

14

Stating the Main Idea

Seeing how your ideas are related will help you begin to write.

WARMUP

Elena wanted to write about her grandmother. She narrowed her topic until she had the following list:

> born in Mexico
> had dark hair
> always there
> made special things to eat
> told great stories about her early life
> loved to tease us
> sang to us in Spanish
> died last year

These were all details about her grandmother, but when Elena looked at the list, she still wasn't sure exactly what she wanted to say. She didn't know where to begin or what she wanted the point of her paragraph to be.

She read over the list again, trying to see what the details had in common. Then she noticed that all but the first two details described things that she liked about her grandmother—things that she really missed since her grandmother died. She decided that the feeling of emptiness was going to be the **main idea** of her paragraph. She wanted every sentence in the paragraph to help the reader understand this idea.

To help her concentrate on the main idea, she wrote it down like this:

> The purpose of this paragraph is to describe the things about my grandmother that I miss since she died.

After Elena finished writing down the main idea, or purpose, of her paragraph, she looked back again at her list. She decided that the first two items on it didn't go with the main idea. She made up her mind to leave them out when she wrote her paragraph.

Knowing what the main idea of your paragraph is and being sure that all the details in the paragraph are related to it are important steps in writing.

Try It

A. Look over the list below.

chewing raw bones	eating when they want to
playing with humans	exploring
running with other dogs	running
being near the humans they like	

continued . . .

Now check the sentence that best expresses the main idea of the list.

1. The main idea is that animals like to sleep.
2. The main idea is that dogs really enjoy doing certain things.
3. The main idea is that training dogs can be a lot of fun.

B. Read the paragraph below and the sentences that follow. Check the sentence that best expresses the main idea of the paragraph.

> George's body was more than six and a half feet long, and he didn't seem to know what to do with a single inch of it. He stooped. He slouched. He shuffled. He twisted his bony arms and legs into pretzels.

1. I had never seen George before.
2. George was as awkward as he was tall.
3. George's friendship was important to me.

C. Read the paragraph below and decide what the main idea is. This time, fill in the blanks in the statement of the main idea with your own words. You can use one or more words in each blank.

> Their extreme hostility—to each other as well as to strangers—has startled every visitor to their desolate planet. The slightest look or remark can provoke an attack. Togobi parents even ignore the cries of their frightened or hungry children. Togobi children, in turn, mistreat their pets.

The main idea is that _____ are not _____.

When Elena first jotted down the main idea of her paragraph, she knew that she wasn't going to use those exact words in her writing. After she thought about it for a while, she decided that she wanted to put her main idea into a sentence that she could include in her paragraph. After a couple of tries, she wrote the following sentence.

> My grandmother's place in our house is empty now, and no one else can fill it.

She liked the sentence because it stated the main idea well and because all the details she had chosen could be connected to it. She planned to use it to start her paragraph.

A sentence in a paragraph that expresses the main idea is called a **topic sentence**. It serves as a guide to the reader. It also guides the writer. It can help the writer get started on the actual job of writing. Paragraphs are often made up of topic sentences followed by other sentences that fill in the details.

Although every good paragraph has a main idea, it does not always need one topic sentence. Many good paragraphs are made up of sentences that all together make up the main idea.

16

Try It

Read this paragraph and decide what the main idea is. Then, read the sentences below and check the one that would make the best topic sentence for this paragraph.

> ... It squatted in the clearing, so low that it didn't seem to have been built for human beings. Rough gray stones covered the outside. The roof hung almost to the ground, and the front door and windows were in shadow. A thorny hedge surrounded it and made it impossible to reach the door knocker.

1. We had been lost in the woods for hours.
2. The house looked strange and unfriendly.
3. I was tired and wanted to rest.

PRACTICING THE PROCESS

Lee's Paragraph

Lee looks at the list he wrote at the end of the last class:

> no heat
> alarm didn't ring
> no clean shirts
> couldn't find my homework

He tries to find what all the things on the list have in common. Then he writes:

> The purpose of this paragraph is to describe one of the worst days of my life.

But he doesn't know what to do next. His teacher suggests that one way to find out what he wants to say is to answer one of these questions:

> Do you like the people, places, or things you are writing about?
> Do you dislike them?
> Do they make you laugh?
> Do they make you feel sad?
> Do they make you angry?
> Do they make you happy?
> Are they funny?
> Are they scary?

Lee revises the statement of his main idea so that it looks like this:

> The purpose of this paragraph is to describe how funny one of the worst days of my life was.

Your Paragraph [WP]

Look again at the list you made on page 14. Then complete this statement:

The purpose of this paragraph is to describe _____

_____ .

Now read your statement over. Is it focused enough so that you know what you want to say next? If not, try focusing it by answering one of these questions:

Do you like the people, places, or things you are writing
   about?
Do you dislike them?
Do they make you laugh?
Do they make you feel sad?
Do they make you angry?
Do they make you happy?
Are they funny?
Are they scary?

If you have changed your statement, rewrite it here.

The purpose of this paragraph is to describe _____

_____

Adding Details

A good description uses lots of details.

WARMUP

The more you have to say about your subject, the more interesting your paragraph will be. When you were looking for an idea to write about, you made lists of words to help you get started. Now you need additional details for your paragraph. You can make lists again, or you can try one of the following methods to help you think of more things to say.

The first warmup is a special kind of exercise called **free writing**. In free writing, you write everything you can think about a subject for a short period of time. You don't stop writing even if you think you have nothing to say. Just keep putting down words—no matter what.

You don't have to worry about making sentences, and you don't have to connect your ideas. You can just write groups of words and ideas. To make things easier for you when you look at your free writing again, leave a space between groups.

Here's what free writing looks like. Consuela's subject was birthday parties.

> Exciting! Want a pink cake next year
> ~ What else ~
> clothes games dancing
> make sure there are enough boys next year
> I don't know what else to write
> maybe a pizza party I wish I had a
> July birthday Judy had fireworks
> best-ever present - the canoe trip

Try It

Choose a subject from the list on the next page and write without stopping until all the lines below it are filled. If you get stuck, write something like "I can't think" or the name of the subject until more thoughts come to you.

> Don't think about making sentences.
> Don't think about punctuation.
> Just focus on writing for the entire time.

continued...

Here's the list.

sneakers	green things	a movie plot	eating pizza
singing	swimming	taking tests	summer jobs
my hobby		soft things	

Remember to write without stopping and fill all the lines.

SUBJECT I CHOSE: _____

FREE WRITING: _____

_____

_____

_____

_____

_____

_____

_____

_____

The second warmup teaches you to ask questions about the subject. When reporters ask questions, they get facts for their stories. Writers can learn to ask themselves questions to get more details. Here's a topic that Mark was asked to write about.

The Day Dr. Martin Luther King, Jr., Was Shot

Before he started to read anything about the subject, he wrote these questions.

Who was there?
What kind of day was it? Weather, temperature.
Who was with Dr. King?
How soon did the country find out?
How did my parents feel about it?
What did the President say?

Try It

Choose one of the topics on the list below. Think about what you would like to know about it. Think about what your readers would like to know. Write questions that will lead to more details.

a police officer's day	aerobic exercise	birds in a snowstorm
becoming an astronaut	a perfect day	a dog's life
using computers in school	making a record	

continued . . .

SUBJECT I CHOSE: _____

QUESTIONS I WANT ANSWERED: _____

_____

_____

_____

_____

_____

The third warm-up shows you another way to make a list of details. When you apply for a driver's license, you have to give some information about what you look like.

Try It

A. Check the appropriate box.

Eyes: Brown _____ Green _____ Blue _____ Black _____
Hair: Brown _____ Black _____ Red _____ Blond _____ Gray _____
Height: 5'-5'4" _____ 5'5"-5'9" _____ 5'10"-6'2" _____
Weight: 100-120 _____ 125-150 _____ 160-180 _____ 190-210 _____
Sex: Male _____ Female _____

Look around the room and find someone about your height with the same color hair and eyes. Fill in the chart below with descriptions that show what makes each of you different. Remember that the more details you put in, the better the description will be. There might be five people in the room with brown hair and brown eyes, but only Francine has "wavy hair that is cut shorter than most boys' hair" and only Fred has "green-tinted glasses with silver frames."

YOUR NAME: _____   NAME OF OTHER PERSON: _____

Hair _____   Hair _____

Eyes _____   Eyes _____

Special Characteristics   Special Characteristics

1. _____   1. _____

2. _____   2. _____

3. _____   3. _____

B. Your cousin from Little Rock is coming to visit you. She hasn't seen you in five years. Using the list you made, think how you can describe yourself so that she will be able to spot you immediately. Then fill in the missing part of the letter.

> 346 Park Street
> Chicago, Illinois
> May 11, 1986
>
> Dear Yolanda,
>
>   Thanks for letting us know what bus you'll be on. I'm going to be there to meet you and take you home. Since we haven't seen each other in a long time—and I haven't sent any photos—let me tell you what to look
>
> for. You can recognize me by _____
>
> _____
>
> _____
>
>   See you on Saturday,

PRACTICING THE PROCESS

Lee's Paragraph

Lee needed to write a second list. The first list he wrote helped him get an idea for his paragraph. When he wanted to start writing about his bad day, he found that he needed more facts. His teacher suggested that he try asking questions that would help him get ideas for free writing.

Lee wrote these questions:

> How many things went wrong?
> What was the worst thing that happened?
> Why do I think they're funny now?
> How did the day begin?
> How did the day end?
> Was it just one thing or a combination of things?

Lee's free writing looked liked this.

at bedtime realized it was April Fool's Day   Mom used current events newspaper clipping in the cat box   socks didn't match   shirts still wet dryer on the blink   Jib used last of breakfast cereal for pigeon food   broken shoelaces   broke glasses in gym surprise math quiz   already 30 minutes late for school when I woke up   house freezing no heat, no hot water   no chance for shower couldn't play basketball   fight with girlfriend

---

Your Paragraph WP

Look back at the purpose of your paragraph (p. 18) and at your list of things you wanted to include in the paragraph (p. 14). Use one or more of the warmup techniques you have practiced in this Lesson to add details to your list. (If you're describing someone, remember to put down all the things that make that person special or different.)

Choose one or more of the following:

QUESTIONS

_____

_____

_____

_____

_____

SPECIAL CHARACTERISTICS

_____

_____

_____

FREE WRITING

_____

_____

_____

_____

_____

Telling Things in Order

Your ideas make sense when you tell them in order.

WARMUP

Ronald is planning to describe the monster he saw in a movie. His list of details isn't in any special order, and he's wondering what to begin with. He thinks about what the monster head looked like and decides to begin his description at the top of the head. Here is what Ronald writes:

> The top of the Mogum's head is round and shiny and completely without hair. That's not so unusual, but as soon as you look down a little, things change. In the middle of its forehead is a lumpy green knob with an eye on the end of it. Just below the eyestalk is something that could be a mouth—a jagged hole filled with needle-like teeth. The face ends in a point with slimy things that look like seaweed hanging from it. All together, it's a disgusting sight.

Ronald used **space order** in his paragraph. He described the parts of the monster's head in order from top to bottom.

Try It

Here are some sentences that describe the front of a building. They need to be arranged in space order. Copy them in the order that describes the building from the roof down.

> Five marble steps lead to the porch. The windows in the top row open onto a balcony. The copper roof has turned green with age. Four white pillars with scrolled tops support the balcony. From the open porch, you enter the building through a massive oak door.

_____

_____

_____

_____

_____

Nikki's paragraph describes her dance audition for the spring talent show. She used **time order**, beginning with what happened first.

> I was so nervous that I arrived for the audition fifteen minutes early. I changed my clothes and sat down to wait. Finally it was my turn. The music began, and I started my routine. I was just getting into it when someone said, "Thank you. Next please."

Try It

Here are some sentences that describe a blizzard. They need to be arranged in time order. Copy them in the order that describes the event from beginning to end.

The first few flakes of snow fell slowly. By the end of the afternoon, a foot of snow lay on the ground. Soon the storm began to pick up speed. We knew a storm was coming when the sky suddenly got dark. The snow fell faster, and the wind began to howl.

_____

_____

_____

_____

_____

PRACTICING THE PROCESS

Lee's Paragraph

Lee is ready to put the details for his paragraph in order. Since he is describing an event, he arranges the details in time order—the order in which they happened. Here is his final list:

already 30 minutes late for school when woke up
house freezing
no heat, no hot water
no chance for shower
shirts still wet
dryer on the blink
socks didn't match
broken shoelaces
Tib used last of breakfast cereal for pigeon food
Mom used current events newspaper clipping in the cat box
surprise math quiz
broke glasses in gym
couldn't play basketball
fight with girlfriend
at bedtime realized it was April Fool's Day

Your Paragraph WP

Look at your list of details from Lesson 4. Decide whether they should be arranged in time order or space order.

Then copy them arranged in one of these ways:

first to last   right to left
top to bottom   near to far
bottom to top   far to near
left to right

_____

_____

_____

_____

_____

_____

_____

_____

Congratulations!

This is the last lesson in the **Prewriting** section, but the thinking that you have started to do will continue throughout the writing of your paragraph. In a way there is no division between prewriting and writing. Whenever you search for new things to say and new ways to say them, you are using some of the prewriting techniques you have just learned.

WRITING

Writing is the process of taking your ideas, your lists, your notes, your questions and turning them into a series of connected sentences.

The first few lessons in this section will help you turn your thoughts into sentences by teaching you how good sentences are written. You will learn how to

- Choose the words that say what you mean.

- Make your sentences interesting.

- Organize your ideas so that your readers can understand you easily.

Then you will see how another student puts together the first draft of a descriptive paragraph. Finally, you'll write your own first draft of a paragraph.

Good Sentences/Specific Words

Using specific words makes your writing more interesting.

Read the following descriptions.

It was a <u>nice day</u>. Everyone was happy because the weather turned out to be <u>good</u>. Since we made the time pass by <u>doing some interesting things</u>, even the ride was a lot of fun. We got <u>there</u> at lunch and spent the rest of the afternoon <u>having a terrific time</u>. Although everyone was tired at the end of the day, we agreed that we'd like <u>to do the same thing</u> again next year.

Answer the following questions about what you have just read.

1. What time of year was it?
2. What was the weather like?
3. What did the group do on the bus?
4. What did the group do at the lake?
5. What did the group want to do next year?

Of course, you can't answer any of the questions because the paragraph doesn't use **specific** words. The reader doesn't know if the group went on an ice-skating trip in the dead of winter or a canoe trip in the late spring.

Here are some of the ways the writer could have changed the paragraph to make it more specific. (These words and groups of words have been underscored in the paragraph.)

ORIGINAL	CHANGED
nice day	cold, crisp winter day
good	perfect for skating
doing some interesting things	having a musical talent show
there	to Echo Lake
having a terrific time	playing hockey, practicing figures, and skate dancing
to do the same thing	to have a class skating party

Practice 1

Copy the paragraph, using specific words in place of general words.

_____

_____

_____

_____

_____

Practice 2

In the sentences below, the parts of the sentence that are too general have been underscored. Make each sentence more specific by substituting words and groups of words from the list below. Write your revised sentences.

pulled

bitter

filled with flowering shrubs and trees

warm and pleasant

filled with stories that will make
    you laugh your head off

cartons of books

unbelievably thrilling

frigid

well written and well acted

skinny yellow dog

1. As soon as the movers left, Ronnie unpacked a few things.

_____

2. The child took her hand away from the hot stove.

_____

3. The cold wind brought with it a new sense of winter.

_____

4. As soon as the sun rose, Paul knew it would be a nice day.

_____

5. Driving a snowmobile is great!

_____

6. The two brothers had not spoken since their big fight of two years ago.

_____

7. Noah's garden was beautiful.

_____

8. Read *Boy, Are My Arms Tired*—it's a funny book.

_____

9. Malcolm thought that the play was interesting.

_____

10. The dog was sniffing at the box of groceries.

Practice 3

The underscored words in the sentences below are too general. Use the free writing lines provided to help you think of words or groups of words to replace them. Then rewrite the sentence, using one of your specific words or word groups.

1. Eunice, you're a <u>great</u> cook.

     FREE WRITING _____

     SENTENCE _____

2. Ms. Jackson read us a <u>beautiful</u> poem about the Civil War.

     FREE WRITING _____

     SENTENCE _____

3. Help us put these <u>things</u> on the shelf.

     FREE WRITING _____

     SENTENCE _____

4. <u>Someone</u> had been waiting for the old man a very long time.

     FREE WRITING _____

     SENTENCE _____

5. This book is <u>boring</u>.

     FREE WRITING _____

     SENTENCE _____

6. Jarmine's description of her vacation project was <u>interesting</u>.

     FREE WRITING _____

     SENTENCE _____

7. A <u>hot</u> sun welcomed the travelers to Jamaica.

     FREE WRITING _____

     SENTENCE _____

8. The reviewer should have told us that the play was <u>sad</u>.

     FREE WRITING _____

     SENTENCE _____

9. When no one was looking, the curious child took <u>it</u>.

     FREE WRITING _____

     SENTENCE _____

Good Sentences/Sensory Words

A description makes the reader see, hear, feel, taste, or smell something.

When you write a description, you want your readers to feel as though they are standing in your place. You want them to see what you see, hear what you hear, taste what you taste. To do this, you need words that show what you see, hear, feel, taste, and smell. The following activities will help you think of words that can make these descriptive details vivid.

Practice 1

Each group of sentences is related to one of your senses. From the list on the right and on the next page, choose a word to complete each sentence. Write it in the blank. The first sentence in each group has been completed as an example. More than one word might fit in a blank, and you may use a word more than once.

1. *Touch*

a. The water feels *hot*.

b. The spring air feels _____.

c. Her velvet jacket feels _____.

d. The cat's long fur feels _____.

e. The ice cube feels _____.

2. *Hearing*

a. Oscar's voice *rumbles*.

b. The wind _____.

c. The lost dog _____.

d. The truck's brake _____.

e. The traffic on the highway _____.

3. *Taste*

a. The lemon tastes *juicy*.

b. The peppers taste _____.

c. The ice cream tastes _____.

d. The watermelon tastes _____.

e. The pickle tastes _____.

cool

gleams

slippery

rotten

salty

spicy

squeals

hot

fresh

smooth

soft

glows

flashes

rough

sugary

scratchy

sweaty

howls

continued . . .

4. <u>*Sight*</u>

a. The light in the window _gleams_ .

b. The bonfire _____ .

c. Gert's diamond earring _____ .

d. The silver tray _____ .

e. The mirror _____ .

5. <u>*Smell*</u>

a. That salami sandwich smells _spicy_ .

b. The soap smells _____ .

c. This food smells _____ .

d. The orange smells _____ .

e. Your locker smells _____ .

rumbles

clean

sparkles

flowery

gleams

hums

bitter

glistens

dry

sweet

juicy

yelps

light

heavy

Practice 2

This time you are going to make your own lists of words that describe the way things look, sound, feel, smell, and taste. An example is given for you at the beginning of each list. Add as many other words as you can.

1. <u>*Touch*</u>

velvety _____

_____ _____

_____ _____

2. <u>*Hearing*</u>

clattered _____

_____ _____

_____ _____

3. <u>*Taste*</u>

tangy _____

_____ _____

_____ _____

4. <u>*Sight*</u>

blazing _____

_____ _____

_____ _____

5. <u>*Smell*</u>

dusty _____

_____ _____

_____ _____

Practice 3

Now use one of the words you listed above—or another sense word if you think of one—to complete each sentence below.

1. The baby was startled by the _____ taste of the pickle.

2. Felicia patted the horse's _____ nose.

3. The lights of the airplane _____ in the night sky.

4. The _____ smell of the house faded when we opened the windows.

5. "Let's make it snappy," _____ the coach to the players who were changing their clothes.

6. The explorers wore wide-brimmed hats to protect them from the _____ sun.

7. Can you identify the ingredient that makes this salad so _____?

8. The _____ breeze from the ocean felt good after our long climb.

9. Their shoes _____ against the stone steps as they climbed to the top of the monument.

10. A _____ odor clung to all the old clothes in the trunk.

WRITING 3:

Good Sentences/Comparing

Observing carefully is an important part of writing a description.

The more details you see and use, the better your description will be. One way to focus on descriptive details is to look at the ways in which two things are like each other and the ways in which they are different. The following activities will help you compare things—or show how they are alike—and contrast them—or show how they are different.

Practice 1

Use a word from the list on the right to complete each sentence below.

Example: A ball is <u>like</u> a circle because they are both *round* _____.

1. Feathers are like fur because they are both _____.

2. The book is like a sheet of paper because they are both

_____.

3. A mouse is like an elephant because they are both _____.

4. A toothpick is like a matchstick because they are both

_____.

5. The sun is like a lamp because they are both _____.

gray

smooth

round

bright

skinny

rectangular

Example: The circle is <u>different</u> from the square in *shape*.

6. The ranch house is different from the skyscraper in

_____.

7. A short story is different from a novel in _____.
8. A bluebird is different from a blackbird in _____.
9. An ant is different from a whale in _____.
10. Glass is different from sand in _____.

size

shape

length

texture

color

height

34

Practice 2

For each pair of things below, list five ways in which they are alike and five in which they are different.

Example: <u>BICYCLE/BUS</u>

Alike	**Different**
wheels	open/closed
used for transportation	one person/many
lights	legs/fuel
horn	handlebars/steering wheel
brakes	own/pay fare

1. <u>BOOK/MOVIE</u>

Alike	**Different**
_____	_____
_____	_____
_____	_____
_____	_____
_____	_____

2. <u>TEACHER/PARENT</u>

Alike	**Different**
_____	_____
_____	_____
_____	_____
_____	_____
_____	_____

3. <u>WHAT YOU ARE LIKE NOW/WHAT YOU WERE LIKE AS A CHILD</u>

Alike	**Different**
_____	_____
_____	_____
_____	_____
_____	_____
_____	_____

Practice 3

Complete each pair of sentences below, using your own words.

Examples:

    a. The pigeon, like all city dwellers, *is at home on the streets*

    b. The pigeon, unlike its country cousins, *perches on buildings*

1. a. Roller skates, like ice skates, _____

    _____.

    b. Roller skates, unlike sneakers, _____

    _____.

2. a. A painting, like a drawing, _____

    _____.

    b. A painting, unlike a photograph, _____

    _____.

3. a. A pizza, like a gourmet meal, _____

    _____.

    b. A pizza, unlike many fast foods, _____

    _____.

4. a. Arms, like the branches of a tree, _____

    _____.

    b. Arms, unlike legs, _____

    _____.

5. a. Moonlight, like candlelight, _____

    _____.

    b. Moonlight, unlike sunlight, _____

    _____.

WRITING 4:

Good Sentences/Combining

Sentences are more interesting to read when ideas are combined.

When you turn your list of details into sentences, you sometimes you put your ideas down one after another, in separate sentences, like this:

> The house looked old. It also looked scary. The door was rusted shut. The door was covered with huge patches of cobwebs. There was mold on the door too. Peeling paint also covered the door. Ivy vines had grown up around the porch. Bramble bushes had grown up also.

As you practice the writing process, you'll learn to combine ideas that are alike into one sentence, like this:

> The house looked old and scary. The door, rusted shut, was covered with huge patches of cobwebs, mold, and peeling paint. Ivy vines and bramble bushes had grown up around the porch.

Read the two paragraphs out loud.

The short sentences in the first example make it sound choppy. The sentences are also less interesting since they repeat words and groups of words.

> The house **looked** old. It also **looked** scary. **The door was** rusted shut. **The door was** covered with huge patches of cobwebs. There was mold on **the door** too. Peeling paint also covered **the door**. Ivy vines **had grown up** around the porch. Bramble bushes **had grown up** also.

When you write, try to combine ideas so that you have one sentence instead of two or three sentences that repeat words.

Practice 1

Rewrite each pair of sentences below. Add the underlined part of the second sentence to the first sentence to make one interesting sentence. (An * shows you where to combine the parts. The instructions in parentheses will tell you how to join them smoothly.)

Example: A strong wind blew toward shore*. It <u>took</u> <u>the</u> <u>boats</u> <u>with</u> <u>it.</u> [use **and**]

A strong wind blew toward shore and took the boats with it.

1. The seagull headed for the fishing boat*. The seagull <u>soon</u> <u>turned</u> <u>out</u> <u>to</u> <u>sea</u>. [use **but**]

   _____

   _____

2. Three fishing boats had left at dawn *. They had <u>returned</u> <u>at</u> <u>sunset</u>. [use **and**]

   _____

   _____

continued . . .

3. At the end of each day, the dockworkers * bought the extra fish. The townspeople also bought fish. [use *and*]

_____

_____

4. Mackerel is a tasty * fish. It is oily too. [use **but**]

_____

5. Shrimp * should be cooked quickly. Lobster should be cooked quickly. [use *and*]

_____

_____

6. Scientists have found that fish is low in calories*. It keeps people healthy. [use *and*]

_____

_____

7. A diet that is made up of a lot of fish * is a good one to follow. Whole grains are good too. So is fruit. Fresh vegetables are good also. [use commas plus *and*]

_____

_____

8. As more and more people learn to eat fish, commercial fishing * will grow in popularity. Private fishing will also grow in popularity. [use *and*]

_____

_____

9. Someone who knows how to use a fishing rod * is a good companion on a vacation. So is someone who knows how to find the best fishing spots. [use *or*]

_____

_____

10. More people will be able to catch their own dinner *. They will be able to relax at the same time. [use *and*]

_____

_____

Practice 2

The ideas in sentences can be combined in more than one way. Combine the ideas in each group of sentences below to make one interesting sentence. Then make another sentence, combining the ideas in a different way.

Example: The house was deserted. It was old. It looked scary.
Combination 1: *The deserted old house looked scary.*
Combination 2: *The scary old house was deserted.*

1. The man who lived in the house was lonely. He was old. He was gray-haired.

_____

_____

2. The shed was painted red. Last night it was broken into. It was where we kept the boat.

_____

_____

3. A monster leaped across the stage. It was made of green rubber. It was hairy and it shrieked.

_____

_____

4. There were hungry wolves in the forest. They were the ones that howled at night.

_____

_____

5. Sidney never left the house. He stayed home because he was afraid of the wind. He is my weird friend.

_____

_____

Good Sentences/Varying

Sentences are more interesting to read when they don't all sound the same.

Often, the easiest kind of sentence to write is one that sounds like this: "The quick red fox jumped over the lazy brown dog." There is nothing wrong with this sentence, and there is no reason that you shouldn't write many sentences like it. But if you write too many sentences like this in a row, your writing will not be as interesting as it could be. To keep your readers interested, you need to vary the way your sentences begin and the way they are put together. Sometimes this involves combining sentences. Here is an example:

SENTENCES ALL ALIKE

   The robot is five feet tall. It weighs 37 pounds. It is mounted on wheels. A motor enables it to move around. It is a great pingpong player. It has been programmed to serve the ball with a spin. Championship players use the robot to practice with now.

SENTENCES VARIED

   The robot is five feet tall and weighs 37 pounds. Mounted on wheels, it has a motor that enables it to move around. The robot is a great pingpong player, programmed to serve the ball with a spin. Now championship players use the robot to practice with.

The following activities will help you vary the way your sentences begin and the way they are put together.

Practice 1

Rewrite each sentence below. Make the underlined part the beginning of the sentence.

Example: Sam read the advertisement slowly and carefully.

Slowly and carefully Sam read the advertisement.

1. Dorothy asked for another chance in a quiet voice.

2. Leonard was exhausted by the end of the day.

3. Coach Grabowski repeated the rules firmly.

4. Terry changed her mind when she heard the announcement.

5. Richard walked quickly to the end of the pier.

---

continued . . .

6. Norma made a list <u>before</u> <u>going</u> <u>to</u> <u>the</u> <u>store</u>.

_____

7. I've been around longer than you have <u>after</u> <u>all</u>.

_____

8. You push this button <u>to</u> <u>find</u> <u>out</u> <u>the</u> <u>right</u> <u>answer</u>.

_____

9. Yolanda opened the package <u>with</u> <u>trembling</u> <u>hands</u>.

_____

10. Miles shouted with joy, <u>zigzagging</u> <u>down</u> <u>the</u> <u>mountainside</u>.

_____

Practice 2

Rewrite each sentence below. Use the words given to begin your new sentence.

Example: A stranger was at the door.

       There was a stranger _at the door._ _____.

1. A pile of dirty clothes was under the bed.

   Under the bed was _____.

2. Someone is outside repairing the telephone lines.

   There is someone_____.

3. Two patients are waiting to see Dr. Vaccaro.

   There are two patients _____.

4. The missing letter lay on her desk.

   On her desk lay _____.

5. Three things were on his mind.

   There were three things _____.

Practice 3

Rewrite each pair of sentences below as one sentence. Use the words given in parentheses to combine them.

Example: Sue couldn't hear. She asked Ms. Josephs to repeat the directions. (*so*)

Sue couldn't hear, so she asked Ms. Josephs to repeat the directions.

1. George was furious. Everything had gone wrong. (**because**)

   _____

2. Look in the telephone book. Find their number. (**to**)

   _____

3. The storm had ended. The air was clear. (**and**)

   _____

4. Julia left the house. The telephone rang. (**before**)

   _____

5. The dog always begs. We are eating dinner. (**while**)

   _____

6. Harvey can't finish his homework without help. Nobody minds. (**but**)

   _____

7. Edwin promised to call. He got home. (**as soon as**)

   _____

8. Handle the plates carefully. Avoid breaking them. (**to**)

   _____

9. Florence stayed inside. She felt better. (**until**)

   _____

10. We'll take Michael home now. He can get to bed early. (**so**)

   _____

Opening Sentence

Real writers hook their readers.

WARMUP

No one wants to continue reading when the first sentence is dull. A good paragraph can begin with an interesting topic sentence, or it can begin with a sentence that doesn't express the main idea but is there to get your attention.

Which sentence makes you want to know what happens next?

Roberta was exhausted.

"Why did I think it would be easy?" Roberta asked herself, gasping for breath.

Both sentences tell you the same thing, but they tell you in different ways. The first sentence just says that Roberta was exhausted. The second one shows you how Roberta felt, and you have to figure out for yourself how tired she is. Figuring it out gets you involved in how Roberta feels—gets you hooked—and makes you want to read more.

What are other ways to hook your readers? Asking a question, the way we just did in this paragraph, is one. Compare these openings:

No one likes the school lunches.

How would you like to eat lukewarm spaghetti and flabby french fries at 10:30 in the morning?

Try It

Here are two paragraph openings. Rewrite each one and make it more interesting by using a question.

1. A flea market is an interesting place to shop.

_____

_____

2. A perfect double play is very hard to make.

_____

_____

Another way of making an opening more interesting is to be more specific. Say who doesn't like the school lunches and what it is they want:

Nine out of ten students at Elmore Junior High School would like fresh fruit and salad added to the lunch menu.

Try It

Here are two more paragraph openings. Rewrite each one and improve it by making it more specific.

    1. No one likes to work all the time.

_____

_____

    2. You can always find something to write about.

_____

_____

You can also begin a paragraph in a dramatic or humorous way to get your readers' attention:

    Students at Elmore Junior High School wonder who will be the first one to die of food poisoning.

Try It

Rewrite these two paragraph openings and improve them by making them more humorous or dramatic.

    1. The other day, Rosa slipped on a banana peel.

_____

_____

    2. None of Edward's grades were very good this marking period.

_____

_____

Another way is to begin with someone saying or doing something that shows rather than tells what the situation is.

    "I hate wasting all this food, but it's not fit to eat," said Roberta as she dumped her lunch in the trash barrel.

Try It

Rewrite these two paragraph openings. Improve them by making them show rather than tell.

1. The first day of summer vacation is a relief.

_____

_____

2. I got some bad news the other day.

_____

_____

PRACTICING THE PROCESS

Rhonda's Paragraph

Rhonda is writing a paragraph about her singing group for the yearbook. When she wrote her list of details, this is what she put down as her main idea:

The purpose of this paragraph is to describe how terrific The Sisters look when they perform.

She decides not to write a topic sentence, but to turn her purpose into an opening sentence that will catch the readers' attention. This is the sentence she writes.

The Sisters look terrific when they perform.

She writes a few more sentences, then stops to think. She looks at her opening sentence again. "The Sisters are a lot more exciting than this sentence," she thinks.

She writes another opening sentence. This time she adds some details to make her description more specific:

The Sisters look terrific when they sing and dance in their sequined dresses.

"It's getting there, but it could still be better. I want to show how exciting The Sisters are," Rhonda says. Finally she decides on this opening sentence:

With sequins and feathers flying, The Sisters tap their way onto the stage.

Your Paragraph [WP]

Find the main idea you wrote for your paragraph. (You can find it on page 18.) It begins "The purpose of this paragaph is . . . "

Now write three possible opening sentences for your paragraph. Be sure to use as many specific words and details as you can in each one.

1. Make the opening sentence a question.

_____

_____

2. Make the opening sentence dramatic or humorous.

_____

_____

3. Make the opening sentence show rather than tell something.

_____

_____

Select the one you like best and use it to begin your paragraph.

Writing the Body

Your list of details gives you the body of the first draft.

WARMUP

When you have a list of details arranged in the order you want them, you are ready to begin writing the body of your paragraph. The body is the part that contains all the details.

The first time you write your sentences is called the **first draft**. You may not be absolutely sure of everything you want to say when you write the first draft, but that's all right. The first draft can be changed as much as you want it to be.

Here is a list of details that have already been put in order—in this case from loud to soft—and one way to turn them into sentences.

music blasting	potato chips being eaten
loud voices	soda being poured
balloons popping	dancing feet
people laughing	whispered conversations in corners
popcorn underfoot	

At first all you can hear are loud voices and the music blasting. When you get a little bit used to the noise, you can pick out the sound of people laughing. Every so often you hear a balloon pop. A few minutes later you can even tell the difference between the crunch of popcorn underfoot and the crunch of potato chips in people's mouths. The softest sounds of all are the glug-glug-glug of soda being poured, the shush-shush of dancing feet, and the quiet whispers of couples in the corners.

Try It

A. Here is a list of details that describe the sounds you hear at a basketball game. They have also been arranged in order from loud to soft. Turn them into sentences of your own. You can put more than one detail in a sentence.

1. crowd cheering	4. players shouting	7. ball smacking against boards
2. loud voices	5. cheerleaders cheering	8. people eating popcorn
3. referee's whistle	6. players' feet thumping	9. people taking off coats

_____

_____

_____

_____

_____

_____

continued . . .

B. Here is another set of details that have been arranged in order. They describe what you see as you step onto an empty beach. Use your own words to turn them into sentences. Remember to combine ideas and vary the way your sentences are put together to make them interesting.

wide stretch of sand   clam and mussel shells
grass sticking up from sand hills   smooth pebbles
empty   wet sand near water's edge
strands of seaweed   waves breaking and rolling in

_____

_____

_____

_____

_____

_____

_____

_____

PRACTICING THE PROCESS

Rhonda's Paragraph

Rhonda is now ready to write the first draft of her paragraph. She already has the opening sentence:

With sequins and feathers flying, The Sisters tap their way onto the stage.

Her list of details has been arranged in the order in which the audience notices them.

high-heeled tap shoes
hats with feathers and veils
snapping fingers
day-glo dresses—satin and sequins
huddle—spring apart
go to different parts of stage
strut back
form chorus line
turn sideways to audience—look over shoulder

This is the first draft Rhonda wrote by adding the body of her paragraph to the opening sentence:

> With sequins and feathers flying, The Sisters tap their way onto the stage. Each Sister wears a differant day-glo color. And high-heeled shoes to match. You can get clothes in all kinds of day-glo colors now. Fingers snapping, they come together in a huddle. Then they spring apart. They go to different parts of the stage. Struting back, they form a chorus line, they turn sideways to the audience and look over there shoulders.

Rhonda rereads what she has written. There are some things she's still not sure about.

1. She thinks that some of the sentences could be combined or rearranged to make the paragraph more interesting.
2. She's not sure that all the sentences really belong.
3. She doesn't think **parts** is the right word, and she would like a more interesting word than **go**, but she can't think of better words right now.
4. She also knows that some of her spelling and punctuation probably needs to be fixed.
5. Most important, she needs to write a final sentence.

She's decided to put the paragraph aside for now and work on it some more later on.

Your Paragraph 📝

On the next page, copy the opening sentence you wrote on page 46. Then using the list of details you wrote on page 26, write the body of your paragraph. Don't write the closing sentence now—you'll be writing that in another lesson. **REMEMBER THAT THIS IS A FIRST DRAFT.** In some ways it is like the freewriting exercise you did earlier. The important thing is to write, even if you're not absolutely sure of what you want to say. It doesn't have to be perfect. You'll get lots of chances to make any changes you want. (So that it will be easier to make changes later on, write on every other line.)

continued . . .

WRITING 8:

Adding More Details

The process of writing sometimes makes you think of something new to say.

WARMUP

Luis has almost finished writing his paragraph, which describes his school on a Monday morning:

> It's hard to know, at first, what kind of place this is. The maze of gray corridors seems to lead nowhere. Every once in a while, a bell rings and doors open. The inhabitants of this strange place file out and shuffle down the corridors. Their faces are pale, and their eyes are blank. At some unknown signal, they go through other doors and disappear until the bell rings again.

Everything he's written so far has been taken from his list of details. He has a few details left that he can use for a closing sentence, too. As he reads over what he has written, though, the description makes him think of some other things that he hadn't put on his original list of details. He decides to add a sentence that will give his readers an additional clue to the identity of the people he is describing:

> It's hard to know, at first, what kind of place this is. The maze of gray corridors seems to lead nowhere. Every once in a while, a bell rings and doors open. The inhabitants of this strange place file out and shuffle down the corridors. Their faces are pale, and their eyes are blank. **They all have sacks of some kind on their shoulders.** At some unknown signal, they go through other doors and disappear until the bell rings again.

When you write your list of details in the prewriting stage, you can't always anticipate everything you'll want or need to say. As you write the body of your paragraph, new ideas may occur to you, or you may find that you overlooked something the readers need to know.

The sentence in dark type shows what Jeannine added to the body of her paragraph just before she finished writing it:

> If I could make a music video for the song "Breakaway," it would begin with just lights flashing on an empty stage. Then there would be a closeup of a guy singing the song. The lights would fade, and he would be alone on a street. A girl would come down the street, and the two of them would dance. **The lights would start coming back on, getting brighter and brighter.** When the lights were all flashing again, she would just stop dancing and walk away. He would be left alone again.

51

Try It

In each group of sentences below, there is a blank where more details could be added. Following the instructions in parentheses, write another sentence in the blank.

1. That dog looked mean enough to take on the whole world._____

    _____

    All its features were pulled back or flattened—its ears, its eyes, its mouth. From the mouth, two rows of sharp teeth protruded.
    (Add something about how the dog held its head.)

2. No one thinks snow is pretty in the city. It starts to turn gray on its way down from the sky._____

    _____

    Then everyone walks on it, turning it into an unappetizing slush.
    (Add something about what happens when the snow hits the sidewalk.)

3. The Turners must have spent a fortune on that party. Table after table was loaded down with cold cuts, sandwiches, salads, fruit, cake, and cookies._____

    _____

    Was there anything to eat or drink that they didn't think of?
    (Add something about what there was to drink.)

4. People say that pets start to look like their owners after a while. I have a friend whose notebook has started to look like him. Donald's clothes are loose and flap when he walks. His notebook has a cover that's about to fall off._____

    _____

    Donald's notebook is bulging and has old test and homework assignments sticking out of it.
    (Add something about how Donald looks that leads into the next sentence.)

PRACTICING THE PROCESS

Rhonda's Paragraph

When Rhonda rereads her paragraph, she starts to see again how The Sisters look when they perform and what makes audiences enjoy them so much. She's described the opening of their routine, but she realizes that she has left out something important: how The Sisters work with the music. She adds a sentence to the body of her first draft, so that it looks like this:

With sequins and feathers flying, The Sisters tap their way onto the stage. Each Sister

wears a different day-glo color. And high-heeled shoes to match. You can get clothes in all kinds of day-glo colors now.
They pick up the beat of the drums.
Fingers snapping, they come together in a huddle. Then they spring apart. They go to different parts of the stage. Strutting back, they form a chorus line, they turn sideways to the audience and look over there shoulders.

Your Paragraph WP

Look again at the first draft you wrote on page 50. Does reading it make you think of anything else you want to add? Use these questions as a guide for adding more details:

- Is the description as complete as you want it to be? Have any details been left out?
- Will your description make sense to readers? Is there anything else they need to know?

If you decide to add a sentence to the body of your paragraph, draw an arrow like this (∫)to show where you want to insert it, and write it in above the line.

Sticking to the Main Idea

What you leave out is as important as what you put in.

WARMUP

The more details you can think of to put in a paragraph, the more interesting your writing will be. You just have to make sure that all the details are related to your main idea.

Read this paragraph.

> The discovery of a diary in a Kansas City attic began a new phase in American history. Up until that time, scholars did not know what it was like for the women who went West on the pioneer trail. ***One of the most traveled routes West was the Oregon trail, which started in the Midwest and ended on the Oregon coast.*** The Kansas City diary was a detailed record of one woman's thoughts and feelings. It was so interesting that historians began hunting all over for diaries and letters. ***Diaries are very personal and say things that shouldn't be read.*** As more and more are found and published, we have a clearer picture of family life in the nineteenth century.

How the discovery of a diary changed the way we think about the lives of pioneer women is the main idea of the paragraph. The two sentences in dark type are interesting sentences, but they have nothing to do with this main idea. They don't belong in the paragraph.

The first sentence in dark type tells more about the trails mentioned in the sentence right before it. The second sentence in dark type tells how the writer feels about diaries. In both cases the ideas are connected to ideas in another sentence, but not to the main idea of the paragraph.

The following activity will help you spot sentences that don't belong.

Try It

Read each paragraph. Find the one sentence in each paragraph that doesn't belong and draw a line through it.

1.   Imagine what a life without homework would be like. Each class would be followed by a study period so that extra work could be done right away. There would be more time for after-school activities—like putting out a newspaper or putting on plays. It takes a lot of time to rehearse and build the sets for a play but it is usually worth it and it's always a lot of fun. Families would have nothing to fight about in the evening. Students would never learn how to invent believable excuses. Maybe homework serves a purpose after all.

---

continued . . .

2. How would you feel if you won a prize in a state lottery? Many people say that if they could win something, their lives would change. However, most of the people who win big prizes try not to change their lives at all. The big prizes are really fantastic, too—you can become a millionaire overnight or get money to travel all year round or win a luxury car. One winner said that she didn't want to lose any of her old friends, so she wasn't even going to quit her job in the supermarket. I'm not sure what I'd do, but I hope I get the chance some day to find out.

3. Ronnie had planned her special day for weeks. Exams were over and she didn't start her summer job for two days. It was her first job—helping out at a day camp —and she was really looking forward to it. On Friday night she would stay out late and not set the alarm. On Saturday she would sleep until she woke up and then she would have fresh orange juice, home-made muffins, and tea. Then she would finish the book she was reading, take a long hot bath, and meet her friends at the movies. At the end of the special day she would feel rested, relaxed, and ready to begin something new.

PRACTICING THE PROCESS

Rhonda's Paragraph

After doing the Try It for this lesson, Rhonda takes a look at the paragraph she wrote.

With sequins and feathers flying, The Sisters tap their way onto the stage. Each Sister wears a differant day-glo color. And high-heeled shoes to match. You can get clothes in all kinds of day-glo colors now. They pick up the beat of the drums. Fingers snapping, they come together in a huddle. Then they spring apart. They go to different parts of the stage. Struting back, they form a chorus line, they turn sideways to the audience and look over there shoulders.

She realizes that one sentence doesn't belong. Can you tell which one it is?

That's right. She crosses out the sentence that says you can get clothes in all kinds of day-glo colors. When she reads her draft again, she feels sure that all her sentences are about one thing—the way The Sisters capture the attention of the audience.

Your Paragraph

Read your first draft again. (p. 50) Do all the sentences belong? Cross out any sentence that doesn't. Now read your draft out loud but to yourself. If your paragraph passes the ear test, then all the sentences are probably about one thing. If you're not sure, ask your teacher.

Closing Sentence

Real writers leave their readers with something to think about.

WARMUP

The ending of a good description makes you think about what you've just read.

Here are three methods writers use to end paragraphs:

- Asking a question
- Adding a personal opinion
- Stating the main idea in another way

One way isn't necessarily better than another. It just depends on what the writer is trying to say.

Try It

A. Read the paragraph below. Then read each of the ways the writer could have chosen to end it. Write the name of the method from the list above.

> If you went into Will's room without a map, you might never find your way out again. His clothes were all over the floor, the bed, and the chair. They were even on his desk. That must have been why all his books and papers were on the floor, along with all his games and hobbies and a lot of other things no one could identify.

FIRST ENDING: Just looking at the mess made me want to go get a shovel.

METHOD: _____

SECOND ENDING: How could someone who looked so neat be such a slob?

METHOD: _____

THIRD ENDING: It was like an unexplored jungle.

METHOD: _____

B. Here's your chance to practice writing endings. Complete each of the following paragraphs in the two ways called for.

1. Every time the train was late, Martin got impatient. He muttered under his breath. Opening his book bag, he took out the time table. He ran his finger over the lines of type, checked his watch, and looked down the empty track.

Restate the Main Idea

_____

_____

continued . . .

Ask a Question

_____

_____

2. As soon as I saw the hill, I knew that the worst part of the race had just begun. My side hurt, and my legs seemed made of lead. Sweat poured from my scalp, and yet my mouth was still dry. Even my arms seemed ready to disobey me.

Add a Personal Opinion

_____

_____

Ask a Question

_____

_____

PRACTICING THE PROCESS

Rhonda's Paragraph

Rhonda takes out the first draft of her paragraph:

With sequins and feathers flying, The Sisters tap their way onto the stage. Each Sister wears a differant day-glo color. And high-heeled shoes to match. ~~You can get clothes in all kinds of day-glo colors now.~~ They pick up the beat of the drums. Fingers snapping, they come together in a huddle. Then they spring apart. They go to different parts of the stage. Struting back, they form a chorus line, they turn sideways to the audience and look over there shoulders.

All she needs to complete it is a good closing sentence. She knows that she can

- Ask a question
- Restate the main idea
- Give her own opinion

She tries a question first:

Don't you think they're terrific?

But she wants to say more than that. She wants to restate the main idea—to sum up in some way everything she's said in the paragraph. This is the sentence she finally writes:

Before you even hear a note, you know how terrific they are going to be.

She adds this sentence to her paragraph.

Your Paragraph [WP]

Try writing a closing sentence for your paragraph in each of these three methods.

1. Restate the main idea.

_____

_____

2. Ask a question.

_____

_____

3. Give your own opinion.

_____

_____

Decide which sentence works best for your paragraph. Then turn back to page 50 and add it to your first draft.

Congratulations!

You have now completed the **Writing** section of this book, and you have a first draft of your description. Now is the time to put it aside for a while—but don't stop thinking about it. There may be some things that you'll decide to change.

REVISING

Revising is really part of writing. Your first draft may not say things exactly the way you would like them to. After you write the first draft, you may change your mind about what you want to say or how you want to say it. Some writers even revise at the same time that they're writing. (You may do this yourself, especially if you use a word processor.)

The first few lessons will help you recognize when sentences need improving and will give you some practice in ways of improving them. Then you will see how another student revises a descriptive paragraph. Finally you will revise your own paragraph.

REVISING 1:

Good Sentences/Completeness

Sentences are easier to understand when they are complete.

A sentence begins with a capital letter and ends with a period. Not every group of words that begins with a capital letter and ends with a period, though, is a sentence. A sentence expresses a thought that can stand alone. Sometimes a group of words that can't stand alone is incorrectly written as though it were a sentence:

> With all my heart.
> Beginning next Tuesday.
> In all the years I've known him.
> Since you went away.
> Waited by the telephone.

What do these groups of words need to make them into sentences? They already have capital letters and periods. In order to be a sentence, each one has to be attached to another group of words that will complete it:

> I love her <u>with all my heart</u>.
> <u>Beginning next Tuesday</u>, things are going to be different around here.
> <u>In all the years I've known him</u>, he's never behaved like this.
> I've felt blue <u>since you went away</u>.
> The heartbroken young man <u>waited by the telephone</u>.

Practice 1

Put a check mark next to each group of words that is incomplete and needs to be attached to another group of words.

____ 1. The editor rejected every one of his articles.
____ 2. Jerome laughed.
____ 3. Shuffling the papers into a big pile.
____ 4. There wasn't an idea left in his head.
____ 5. On his way downstairs in the elevator.
____ 6. A wonderful plan for a new story.
____ 7. He couldn't wait to tell someone.
____ 8. Raced right back upstairs.
____ 9. As soon as he began to explain.
____ 10. The editor smiled and held out her hand.

62

Practice 2

Combine the two groups of words in each item to make a sentence that is complete.

Example: Linda stopped writing. The moment the bell rang.

Linda stopped writing the moment the bell rang.

1. Howard and Harold wearing nothing but red nightshirts. Brought down the house.

_____

_____

2. Filomena carefully poured the batter. Into a greased pan.

_____

3. Arthur walked out of the room. Because he didn't want to hear any more arguments.

_____

_____

4. Taking their time. The Bassetts strolled along the boardwalk.

_____

5. Teena showed up to collect her prize. The day the winners were announced.

_____

_____

6. Has Janette ever told you about her two friends? Nikki and Doreen.

_____

_____

7. My Aunt Ella could teach you anything. Even how to catch a runaway pig.

_____

_____

8. Raymond wrapped a towel around the water pipe. Instead of fixing it.

_____

_____

9. At the edge of the cliff. There was a place to stop and turn around.

_____

10. The part of the movie that I missed. Showed what happened to the parrot.

_____

_____

Practice 3

Add words of your own to make each group of words into a complete sentence.

Example: Into his pocket.

He put his hand into his pocket.

1. All at one time.

_____

_____

2. Humming a funny tune.

_____

_____

3. The books that Melvin ordered.

_____

_____

4. On top of the refrigerator.

_____

_____

5. Since she couldn't make up her mind.

_____

_____

Good Sentences/Conciseness

Sentences are more interesting and easier to understand when they don't contain unnecessary words.

The best sentences contain just the words needed to say what the writer wants to say. There aren't any extra words to confuse or distract the reader. Compare the two sentences in each pair below. Do the words in dark type add anything to the meaning of the sentence?

Dorothy blinked in the bright sunlight.
Dorothy blinked **her eyes** in the bright sunlight.

Dean was late because he missed the bus.
Dean was late because **of the fact that** he missed the bus.

Please see the person in charge of student activities.
Please see the person **who is** in charge of activities **for** students.

Sometimes a writer accidentally repeats an idea that has already been expressed by another word. When you use the word **blink**, for example, you don't need to add **eyes** because **blink** already means to close and open the eyes. Here is another example:

The exam began at 2:30 **p.m. in the afternoon.**

In this sentence, you don't need both **p.m.** and **in the afternoon** because they both mean the same thing. You can use one or the other.

Practice 1

The repeated words in each sentence are underlined. Rewrite the sentence. Leave out the words that are not needed.

Example: The suspect was shot <u>dead</u> and <u>killed</u>.

The suspect was shot dead

or

The suspect was shot and killed

1. Wilma <u>doesn't need</u> all these <u>unnecessary</u> words in her paragraph.

_____

2. Each pumpkin <u>weighed</u> more than twenty pounds <u>in weight</u>.

_____

3. The <u>sparkling glitter</u> of the jewels was reflected in the mirrors.

_____

continued . . .

4. The wrestler's <u>enormous</u> strength was <u>overpowering</u>.

_____

5. Rudy stared at us <u>blankly, with an empty expression on his face.</u>

_____

Writers sometimes use expressions that sound important but don't add anything to the sentence:

What I want to say is that it is important to proofread your work.
Angelo was puzzled because **of the fact that** no one had arrived yet.

Each of these sentences sounds fine without the words in dark type.

Writers also use groups of words that could be shortened:

The bear moved **in a clumsy way** on its hind legs.
The wolf couldn't blow down the house **that was made of brick**.

These sentences have to be rewritten in order to take out the unnecessary words:

The bear moved clumsily on its hind legs.
The wolf couldn't blow down the brick house.

Practice 2

Rewrite each sentence. Leave out the underlined part or shorten it, leaving out any unnecessary words. Rearrange or add new words if you need to.

Examples: <u>The thing is that</u> no one understood what Enrico was trying to say.

No one understood what Enrico was trying to say.

The child <u>who had red hair</u> was always in trouble.

The red-haired child was always in trouble.

1. Why does Marty always pick the card <u>that is on the bottom of the deck</u>?

_____

2. <u>In my opinion</u>, a bad dress rehearsal means a good performance.

_____

3. All the runners <u>who are in the marathon</u> are warming up for the race.

_____

4. Dr. Franconi explained everything <u>in a clear way</u>.

_____

Practice 3

Rewrite the paragraph below. Leave out any unnecessary words. Rearrange or add new words if you need to.

A pair of two brothers who were from Michigan decided to walk around the world. It seems that the trip took them four years. They walked a distance of fifteen thousand miles and used up twenty pairs of shoes. Because of the fact that the Chinese government wouldn't allow them to walk across China, they walked across Australia instead. At the end of their trip, which ended in 1973, they went from California back to their starting point.

_____

_____

_____

_____

_____

_____

_____

_____

REVISING 3:

Good Sentences/Readability

Long, rambling sentences sometimes need to be broken into shorter sentences.

Sometimes when writers start combining details, they forget to stop. They put so many ideas together that one sentence becomes almost as long as a paragraph.

Here's Sarah's first draft.

> The lake was always too cold in the first week of June and even though we knew what to expect the icy water always numbed us and we would come out as quickly as we went in we would run back to the house and there on the porch were steaming mugs of hot cocoa because Aunt Jo always made us hot cocoa on the first swimming day because she remembered how she had felt when she was young.

When she looked at it again, she realized that it went on too long. She added punctuation and capitals to make more sentences. Each line of what she wrote has been numbered to help you see the revisions.

1. The lake was always too cold in the first week of June. and Even though

2. we knew what to expect, the icy water always numbed us. and We

3. would come out as quickly as we went in ~~we would~~ *and* run back to the

4. house. and There on the porch were steaming mugs of hot cocoa. ~~because~~

5. Aunt Jo always made us hot cocoa on the first swimming day because she

6. remembered how she had felt when she was young.

This is what she did.

Line 1: She made her first sentence by adding a period after the word *June*.
She crossed out the word *and* and began her second sentence with *Even*, capitalizing the **e**.

Line 2: She added a comma after *expect* and ended the second sentence by adding a period after *us*.
She crossed out the word *and* and began her third sentence by capitalizing the word *we*.

Line 3: She improved the third sentence by taking out *we would* and putting in *and*.

Line 4: She ended the third sentence with a period after *house*.
She began the fourth sentence by crossing out *and* and capitalizing *There*. She ended the fourth sentence with a period after *cocoa* and crossed out *because*.

Lines 5 and 6: Since *Aunt* already began with a capital letter and since she had already ended with a period, she didn't have to make any more changes for her last sentence.

68

Practice 1

Lu Ann wrote a paragraph. When she revised it, she broke up the rambling sentences into shorter, more interesting sentences. In the lines below her paragraph, write what she did. Follow the examples on the bottom half of p. 68.

I had always wanted to take dancing lessons ~~and it was probably because~~ When I was a baby I won a prize at the church picnic ~~because I was the best dancer~~ and I kept ~~that prize~~ *it* on my night table ~~and I would~~ *to* look at it every night ~~and I would~~ pray to be allowed to take dancing lessons, and when I was eight my prayers were answered.

Line 1 _____

_____

_____

Line 2 _____

_____

_____

Line 3 _____

_____

_____

Line 4 _____

_____

_____

Practice 2

Vince wanted to improve his paragraph by turning his long, rambling sentences into shorter sentences. Do it for him by adding punctuation and crossing out words where necessary.

1. The first canoe trip I ever went on was scary but fun a

2. group of us from school went with our basketball coach to

3. Baron's River and it was a beautiful day the sun was

4. shining and the river seemed peaceful things went

5. smoothly until we reached a patch of white water and

6. the rough water capsized all our canoes fortunately we

7. were all good swimmers and all we got was wet.

Revising the First Draft

Revising gives you a chance to change your mind about what you want to say or how you want to say it.

WARMUP

It is hard to separate revising from writing. Many writers do both at the same time. For example, you might have inserted a sentence or crossed one out while you were writing your first draft. When writers feel unsure about something they are writing, they sometimes leave a blank. They may also write several words to choose from later or make a mark to show they are thinking of changing something.

Bert wrote a first draft of a description of his Aunt Amy. It looked like this:

> Amy (liked to write) (enjoyed writing) poetry. It was the _____ in her life that gave her the most pleasure. But she sometimes had difficulty choosing the right word.

When Bert revised, his paper looked like this:

> Amy (~~liked to write~~) (enjoyed writing) poetry. It was the *activity* in her life that gave her the most pleasure. But she sometimes had difficulty choosing the *exact* ~~right~~ word.

Even when the first draft looks complete, every writer goes back to revise. T. J., for example, has decided to make some changes in the first draft of his paragraph. Here is how he indicated what he wanted to change:

1. (When he talks he doesn't sound like an actor.) He looks so relaxed
2. and natural. Just like he's in his own livingroom. He really
3. remembers what it was like to be a kid. One of his *funniest* ~~favorite~~
4. stories is about the time he was scared in a horror movie. ~~and~~ He
5. had to be taken out of the movies and everyone made fun of him
6. afterwards. *It was an awful thing to happen but he made it sound funny* ~~I wonder if that movie was as scary as Jaws.~~
7. I wish I could tell stories like that about my life and make
8. people laugh.

This is what he did.

Line 1: He moved the first sentence by circling it and using an arrow to show where he wanted it to go.

Line 2: He combined the second and third sentences by changing the period after **natural** to a comma and changing the capital letter in **Just** to a small **j**.

Line 3: He began a new sentence after the word **kid** by adding a period and capitalizing **One**. He changed **favorite** to **funniest** by drawing a line through it and writing the new word above it.

Line 4: He made another new sentence by adding a period after *movie*, crossing out *and* and capitalizing *He*.

Line 6: He crossed out the sentence about the movie *Jaws* because it didn't have anything to do with the main idea. He also decided that he needed another detail. He added a sentence by writing it in above the line.

Try It

Here is a paragraph for you to revise. Use arrows, cross out words, and write in words above the line—just like T.J. did—to show your changes. If you make new sentences, don't forget to change the punctuation.

Look for the following things:

- ideas that need to be combined
- unnecessary words
- words that are too general
- ways to vary the sentence openings
- rambling sentences

What I really like to see in the refrigerator after school is leftover spaghetti. I like it because I like to eat it as a snack with corn bread. I also like to eat sliced pineapple with it. I start by making a layer of corn bread and then I put on a layer of spaghetti and I make sure to spread some of the sauce on the corn bread and then I cover it with another slice of corn bread. I put some slices of pineapple on top of the whole thing. You can't believe how good this tastes!

PRACTICING THE PROCESS

Rhonda's Paragraph

Now that she's had more time to think, Rhonda is ready to revise her paragraph. She has already added a detail and taken out a sentence that didn't belong. Now she's decided to

get rid of an incomplete sentence
combine two sentences
change two words that she doesn't like

Here is what she did.

With sequins and feathers flying, The Sisters tap their way onto the stage. Each Sister wears a differant day-glo color, ~~And~~ *and* high-heeled shoes to match. ~~You can get~~

~~clothes in all kinds of day-glo colors now.~~
They pick up the beat of the drums.
Fingers snapping, they come together in a
huddle. Then they spring apart /\ ~~They~~ ^and^
^twirl^
~~go~~ to different ^corners^ ~~parts~~ of the stage.
Struting back, they form a chorus line,
they turn sideways to the audience
and look over there shoulders. Before
you can hear a note, you know how
terrific they are going to be.

Your Paragraph 🆆🅿

Turn to the first draft of your paragraph on page 50. Read it carefully and think about what you would like to change. Put a check next to each item below that needs to be changed in your paragraph.

____ uses specific words
____ uses vivid words
____ combines ideas
____ varies the way sentences begin
____ varies the way sentences are put together
____ includes enough details
____ sticks to the main idea
____ uses complete sentences
____ doesn't use unnecessary words
____ doesn't use rambling sentences
____ uses an interesting opening sentence
____ uses an interesting closing sentence

Make whatever changes your paragraph needs. Don't worry about spelling for now. You'll get a chance to fix that later.

Another Way of Focusing

Sometimes you don't know what you want to say until after you've written it.

WARMUP

Carla is a professional writer. Right now she's working on a magazine article about how the town of Clarksville fought pollution from a nearby chemical plant. Using the notes from her interviews of local people and the other ideas she's jotted down, she has begun to write a draft of her article. Her first paragraph begins

> The town of Clarksville didn't want to be pushed around anymore.

She has selected the details to show how the people of Clarksville resisted what was happening to them. Her examples include the group of parents who protested to the state department of environmental protection, and she has used words like **stubborn** and **independent** to describe them.

During the process of writing all this, however, Carla finds herself thinking about some of the other ideas in her notes. There is more than one way to describe what happened in Clarksville. Now that she's seen how her description looks written from one point of view, she realizes that she wants a more dramatic way of focusing her story. She takes another sheet of paper and starts a new list of ideas:

> The town of Clarksville **had become a frightening place to live**.

> The town of Clarksville **was famous for the way it smelled**.

Try It

Add some more sentences to Carla's list.

The town of Clarksville knew _____

The town of Clarksville hated _____

The town of Clarksville was filled with _____

Monique has a similar problem. She has started to write a descriptive paragraph called, "What I Don't Like About January." Using the list of details she wrote earlier, she is focusing on "days too short," "waking up in the dark," and "no vacation."

cold	ice
too much snow	too much work
days too short	slush
waking up in dark	boring
no vacation	

As she continues to write, though, it occurs to her that the worst thing about the month of January is how cold she always feels. She writes "I can never get warm in the month of January" at the top of a new sheet of paper. Then she circles the details that she wants to focus on now:

cold   ice

too much snow   slush

Try It

The following details are all related to the same subject. The three statements show three ways to focus on the subject. Under each statement, write four details you would use in a paragraph beginning with that statement. Some details can be used in more than one paragraph.

long lines   roller coaster

fun house   like a holiday

waiting for food   dizzy from rides

hitting the bullseye staying up late

starting out early   eating junk food

being with my friends whirling upside down

parachute jump   shooting gallery

water rides   acting crazy

animal shows   winning a prize

SUBJECT: Why I like spending a day at an amusement park

STATEMENT 1: A day at an amusement park is exciting.

DETAILS: _____

_____

_____

_____

STATEMENT 2: A day at an amusement park is fun.

DETAILS: _____

_____

_____

_____

STATEMENT 3: A day at an amusement park is scary.

DETAILS: _____

_____

_____

_____

PRACTICING THE PROCESS

Rhonda's Paragraph

Rhonda had finished her paragraph, except for some final changes. She reread what she had written and found that she liked it very much. She had shown what The Sisters' costumes were like and how they moved onstage. When she finished reading, she was as ready to hear them sing as someone in the audience would be.

When Rhonda put the paragraph back in her notebook, she found another list of details she had made. It included much more than the list she used for the body of her report:

> hats with feathers and veils
> day-glo dresses—satin and sequins
> ***lean over edge of stage***
> form chorus line
> snapping fingers
> ***beckon to audience***
> high-heeled tap shoes
> ***lowered eyelids***
> turn sideways to audience—look over shoulder
> ***about to share a secret***
> go to different parts of stage
> huddle—spring apart
> ***wink***
> strut back

Because she had focused on how terrific The Sisters look when they perform, she had left out some of these details—the ones shown in dark type. Reading them again, she realized that the details she hadn't used also gave her an interesting way to describe The Sisters—by showing how special they made the audience feel when they performed.

There was no need for Rhonda to rewrite her paragraph, but she liked knowing that there was more than one way to describe The Sisters. Maybe she would write the other description for an article in the school paper.

Your Paragraph WP

Look again at the first list of details you wrote, on page 14, before you focused your paragraph. Do any of these details give you an idea for another way to focus the paragraph? Can you think of any other way you might want to change the focus? Here are some suggestions:

- Emphasize a different part of what you have described.

- Describe the person, place, thing, or event from a different point of view. For example, if you described a show as though you were in the audience, you might want to describe it as though you were one of the performers.

- Give a different reason for liking or not liking what you have described.

In the space below, write one new focus for your paragraph and list some details you could use in writing it.

FOCUS: _____

DETAILS: _____

_____

_____

_____

Congratulations!

You have now written and revised a complete description of something you are interested in. Read it over again, and enjoy it—all writers do that. If you want other people to enjoy reading it, though, there is one more step to complete.

EDITING

Editing is the final step in the writing process. At this stage, you concentrate on making your manuscript look good so that it will be easy to read. You learn some tricks to make proofreading easier. The Editing Handbook helps you check and correct your spelling, punctuation, and usage. Then, using the model for manuscript form, you put the title on your paragraph and write the final copy.

EDITING 1:

Editing Handbook

Writers follow editing rules to make their writing easier to read.

This Handbook will help make your writing easier for others to read. When you edit your writing, check it for

- capitalization
- punctuation
- usage
- spelling

CAPITALIZATION

When a word begins with a capital letter, the reader knows that is special.

Read each rule and then apply it by capitalizing the correct word in the Practice Sentence.

1. Capitalize the first word—

   - *in a sentence*

     The shark is the world's most dangerous fish.

     PRACTICE: what is the most dangerous mammal?

   - *in a quotation*

     Damien asked, "How do you make a movie?"

     PRACTICE: Tom answered, "first, you need a script."

   - *in the greeting or closing of a letter*

     Dear Ms. Jackson:
     Sincerely,

     PRACTICE: very truly yours

2. Capitalize the word *I*.

   "If *I* invite Toya, will she come?"

   PRACTICE: "What do you want?" i asked.

3. Capitalize the *first* word and all the words in a title *except* for short words like <u>a</u>, <u>an</u>, <u>at</u>, <u>for</u>, <u>in</u>, <u>of</u>, <u>the</u>, <u>to</u>.

   The Story of a Lonely Summer
   "Stairway to Heaven"

   PRACTICE: "in the good old summertime"

4. Capitalize words that name or refer to a particular person, place, thing, or group. Here are some examples:

- *Months, days, holidays*

    August, Thursday, Christmas

    PRACTICE: september   friday   thanksgiving

- *Businesses, institutions, government departments*

    Ford Motor Company, Elmore Junior High School, Department of Education

    PRACTICE: general motors   king high school   department of defense

- *Historical events, documents, periods*

    Civil War, Emancipation Proclamation, Nuclear Age

    PRACTICE: revolutionary war   constitution   first world war

- *Brand names*

    Starlite peaches

    PRACTICE: moonglow floor wax

- *Nationalities, languages, geographical names*

    Korean, Swahili, Saigon, Lake Huron

    PRACTICE: italian   vietnamese   kinshasha   mount washington

---

CAPITALIZATION REVIEW

Add a capital letter where you need to in each sentence.

1. how often do you practice?

2. George asked, "when do we begin?"

3. Did i tell you what happened yesterday?

4. Norman was born in september.

5. His mother is an enginer at grimes power company.

6. Jessie's uncle fought in the vietnam war.

7. The funniest commercial on TV shows a dog not eating growlpup dog food.

8. animal trainers need lots of patience and a calm voice.

9. The view from mount wellmont is spectacular.

10. Julio needs practice in spanish conversation.

PUNCTUATION

End Marks

End marks tell the reader where a sentence ends.

Read each rule and then apply it by adding a period or a question mark in the Practice Sentence.

1. When a sentence makes a statement, make sure it ends with a period.

> The battle was fought here**.**

> PRACTICE: The Americans claimed the victory

2. When a sentence asks a question, make sure it ends with a question mark.

> How much do you know about the light bulb **?**

> PRACTICE: Do you know who invented it

Commas

Commas separate words, groups of words, or sentences.

Read each rule and then apply it by adding a comma in the Practice Sentence.

1. When two sentences are combined by a joining word like **and**, **but**, or **or**, make sure there is a comma before the joining word.

> The human spine relaxes during sleep**, and** people are taller in the morning.

> PRACTICE: T. J. is well over six feet tall but his sister Jessica is only four feet eleven inches.

2. When a sentence begins with a long group of words, make sure there is a comma after the group of words that opens the sentence.

> When the first commercial was shown on TV**,** it cost only nine dollars.

> If you want to advertise on TV today**,** you can spend millions.

> In the first six months of last year**,** advertisers spent more on TV than ever before.

> Waiting for the sports news**,** Sanji listened to the weather report.

> PRACTICE: When Toya watches music video she likes to sing along.

>> If you do your homework first you can relax and watch TV.

>> At the end of the day Rollie likes to read.

>> Complaining about the sound Elton turned off the stereo.

3. When you have a list of three or more things in a sentence, make sure there is a comma between each item.

> The cook needed more eggs**,** butter**,** and cheese.

> PRACTICE: Mona likes pepperoni onions and mushrooms on her pizza.

Apostrophes

Apostrophes have special uses.

Read each rule and then apply it by adding an apostrophe in the Practice word.

1. When you write a contraction like <u>isn't</u> or <u>there's</u>, make sure there is an apostrophe.

haven't	there's
isn't	where's
can't	she's
doesn't	you're
aren't	I'll

PRACTICE: They havent told me.   Theres the letter.

It isnt very cold.   Wheres the stamp?

You cant do that.   Shes staying home.

It doesnt mean anything.   Youre angry.

We arent ready to leave.   Hell be there.

2. When you show that something belongs to someone, make sure that you use an apostrophe.

Tyrone's tie	boys' jackets
a judge's decision	two judges' decisions
a woman's right	women's rights

PRACTICE: Borrow Michaels glove.

Senator Chang got all the citizens votes.

Look at that mans hat.

PUNCTUATION REVIEW

Add periods, question marks, commas, and apostrophes where they are needed.

1. When the alarm rang Elena got up

2. Sid wrote about his childhood and Rory wrote about his future plans

3. Did you see the lawyers face when her client lost

4. Geraldo wont do that again and neither will Roma.

5. Theres a piece of the puzzle missing but Sherelle must know where it is.

6. If readers wishes are important why aren't books less expensive to buy?

7. At the end of every exam period we celebrate with pizza doughnuts and fruit punch.

8. Nans coat was caught on a nail but she rewove the torn material.

9. When April comes again Ill remember you.

10. Walking softly the guide came within ten feet of the young deer

USAGE

Ask yourself these questions as you read over your paragraph.

    1. Did I use the correct form of each verb?

    2. Did I use the correct form of each pronoun?

    3. Did I use the correct form of each plural?

SPELLING

Here is a list of commonly misspelled words. Look at each word. Then close your eyes and try to picture the word as if you were seeing it on a chalkboard. Then write the word in the space provided. After you have practiced spelling these words, look at your paragraph and see if you need to make any changes.

1. where _____	24. sincerely _____
2. I'll _____	25. February _____
3. without _____	26. although _____
4. four _____	27. would _____
5. athletics _____	28. accidentally _____
6. which _____	29. their _____
7. very _____	30. during _____
8. library _____	31. believe _____
9. you're _____	32. address _____
10. ready _____	33. weight _____
11. neighbor _____	34. because _____
12. arctic _____	35. we're _____
13. could _____	36. marriage _____
14. your _____	37. attention _____
15. description _____	38. beginning _____
16. decision _____	39. permission _____
17. we'll _____	40. misspelled _____
18. winning _____	41. business _____
19. across _____	42. thought _____
20. happened _____	43. receive _____
21. excellent _____	44. didn't _____
22. special _____	45. completely _____
23. weird _____	46. courageous _____

Proofreading

Proofreading and editing are the last steps you do
before making the final copy.

WARMUP

Use these marks when you proofread.

Capitalize a word.	$\underset{\text{S}}{\text{\$arah}}$
Add punctuation.	Because she needed more information for her paper⸲Sarah went to the library.
Take out a word.	Sarah went to the ~~the~~ library.
Add a word.	Sarah went to $\overset{\text{the}}{\wedge}$ library.
Correct a misspelled word.	Sarah went to the ~~libary~~ *library*.

To train yourself to be a good proofreader, do the following:

- Read sentences word by word.
- Read a word you're not sure of letter by letter.
- Write corrections neatly.
- Read and correct a second time.

PRACTICE

These exercises will help you train your eye so that you can become a better proofreader.

1. Cross out the extra letter.

    seeeing   controllling   plannning   becomming   terrrific

    Dave'ss Kitchen is one of my favorite shows.

2. Cross out the extra word in each sentence.

    Mark hoped to catch the first first show.

    Willis told us about the time he and a a friend of his got scared in the movies.

    In in the beginning of the book, you learn who the murderer is.

    Whenever Josie sees a video she really likes, she she writes a letter to the TV station.

3. Cross out the letters that are reversed and write them correctly above the word.

    Sollie worte a long letter to his mother.

    Get another cup—this one is borken.

    The hiking tirp has been canceled.

    Will you please sotp making so much noise?

PRACTICING THE PROCESS

Rhonda's Paragraph

This is what Rhonda's revised paragraph looked like after she had proofread it.

With sequins and feathers flying, The Sisters tap their way onto the stage. Each Sister wears a ~~different~~ different day-glo color and ~~And~~ high-heeled shoes to match. ~~You can get clothes in all kinds of day-glo colors now.~~ They pick up the beat of the drums. Fingers snapping, they come together in a huddle. Then they spring apart ~~They~~ and twirl ~~go~~ to different corners ~~parts~~ of the stage. Strutting ~~Strutting~~ back, they form a chorus line,. They ~~they~~ turn sideways to the audience and look over their ~~there~~ shoulders. Before you can hear a note, you know how terrific they are going to be.

Your Paragraph WP

Turn to your revised paragraph on page 50. Proofread it by reading it over word by word and —for words you're not sure of—letter by letter. When you think you've caught all the errors, read it again.

Final Copy

The final copy always looks good.

Before making the final copy, Rhonda reviewed the rules her teacher had given to the class.

1. Put a heading in the upper right-hand corner of your paper.
   The heading consists of

   Your name
   Your class
   The date

2. Put the title of the paragraph on a separate line in the center of the page. Follow the rules for capitalizing titles.
3. Leave a margin top and bottom and left and right.
4. Indent your paragraph five spaces or five letters.

Then she wrote her final copy.

Rhonda Jackson
Language Arts
January 3, 1989

Waiting for The Sisters

With sequins and feathers flying, The Sisters tap their way onto the stage. Each Sister wears a different day-glo color and high-heeled shoes to match. They pick up the beat of the drums. Fingers snapping, they come together in a huddle. Then they spring apart and twirl to different corners of the stage. Strutting back, they form a chorus line. They turn sideways to their audience and look over their shoulders. Before you hear a note, you know how terrific they are going to be.

Your Paragraph WP

Write the final copy of your revised and proofread paragraph right here.

_____

_____

_____

_____

_____

_____

_____

_____

_____

_____

_____

_____

_____

_____

_____

_____

Congratulations!

You have now written a paragraph that other people can enjoy reading. What you've learned doesn't stop with this paragraph. You can apply it to other one-paragraph essays or to longer pieces of writing. Whatever kind of writing you do, the process will always be the same—prewriting, writing, revising, and editing.

WRITING PROJECTS: REPORTS

Writing a report about something you have read or seen is a task that you will often be called on to do in school. All of the techniques you learned in writing a paragraph will be used in writing the book or film report. In addition you will learn some of the things you may need to know when you write more than one paragraph:

- organizing the ideas into paragraphs
- writing an outline
- summarizing ideas, events, or stories
- turning an outline into paragraphs

You will discover that no matter how long a piece of writing gets, the **process** is the same —prewriting, writing, and revising.

Organizing Your Ideas

When you write two or more paragraphs, you need to group your ideas.

WARMUP

Now that you know how to write a paragraph, it will be easy to move on to writing a report. A report is made up of several paragraphs that are connected. Together, they share one main idea—the main idea of the entire report. In addition, each paragraph in the report has its own main idea supported by details.

To organize all the details you plan to include in a report, you need to know how to group them. The following activities will give you practice with putting things into categories and with identifying how groups of things are related.

Try It

A. Under each heading on the left, write the words from the list on the right that belong in that group.

Example:

things for cleaning with

soap

sponge

mop

broom

	soap
	plates
	sponge
	mop
	sneakers
	broom
	pillow

1. **kinds of music**

	records
	country and western
	blues
	drums
	reggae
	jazz
	singers

2. **things to drink**

	orange juice
	gasoline
	bread
	tea
	mud
	water
	milk

continued . . .

3. **kinds of buildings**

_____

_____

_____

_____

farmhouse
cottage
door
castle
basement
skyscraper
kitchen

B. The items listed in each group below are related in some way. Write a word or two that names each group. (NOTE: You will probably find more than one name that works.)

Example: hotdogs
pizza
tacos
french fries
hamburgers
food _____

1. screwdriver
   hammer
   wrench
   saw
   drill

   _____

2. cotton
   silk
   wool
   linen
   velvet

   _____

3. paper
   ruler
   pencils
   eraser
   scissors

   _____

4. surgeon
   nurse
   orderly
   X-ray technician
   physical therapist

   _____

Knowing which ideas belong together and how they are related is just the beginning. You also need to plan the way they will be arranged in your report. One way of showing how you intend to organize the ideas in your report is to make an outline. An outline states each main idea and the details that go with it.

For example, if you were writing a report on the neighborhood you live in, you might want one part of it to be about the kinds of buildings in your neighborhood and another part to be about the kinds of people. An outline for these parts of your report might look like this:

I. Kinds of buildings

A. Apartment buildings

B. Stores

C. Post office

91

II. Kinds of people

   A. Families with children

   B. Older people

The Roman numeral **I** shows that **Kinds of buildings** is the first main point. The letters **A, B,** and **C** show that **Apartment buildings, Stores,** and **Post office** are the supporting details that go with **kinds of buildings.** In the same way, the Roman numeral **II** shows what the second main point is, and the letters **A** and **B** show which supporting details go with it.

Try It

Arrange the list below in an outline with two main points. Put two supporting details under one of the main points and three supporting details under the other. Use Roman numerals and letters to show which are the main points and which are the supporting details.

Paper	Box kite
Types of kites	Cloth
Plastic	Kinds of materials
Indian fighter kite	

_____

_____

_____

_____

_____

_____

_____

PRACTICING THE PROCESS

Mario's Report

Mario's class is getting ready to write a special kind of report — the book or film report. The writer of the report describes a book or film and gives reasons for liking or disliking it. If the reports are kept on file, they are a useful way for class members to find out something about the books or films they are interested in reading or seeing.

Mario is planning to write a report on a book he has read and enjoyed—*Star Ka'at* by André Norton and Dorothy Madlee. His teacher has explained that a book or film report has three main parts: the introduction, a summary of the plot, and the conclusion. The introduction gives the title of the book or film, the name of the author or director, and a brief statement of the *theme*, or what the book or film is about. The summary tells what happened, and the conclusion tells whether you liked the book or film and why.

Mario has decided to begin his book report by writing an outline to help him get his thoughts in order. It looks like this:

I. Introduction

    A. Title

    B. Author

    C. Theme

II. Summary

    A. Main characters

    B. Action

III. Conclusion

    A. My opinion

    B. Reasons

Your Report WP

Choose a book you have read recently or a movie you have seen recently and want to write about. (It doesn't have to be a book or film you liked. You may want to write about it because you disliked it and want to let others know that, in your opinion, it is not worth reading or seeing.) Be sure you are familiar enough with the plot to be able to summarize it.

Write the title here: _____

The outline that Mario wrote is a standard one for a book or film report. To help you become familiar with it, copy it on the lines below. You will use it later to help organize the ideas in your paper.

_____

_____

_____

_____

_____

_____

_____

_____

_____

Writing a Summary

A summary gives just the most important ideas
from a longer piece of writing.

WARMUP

An important part of a book or film report is the **summary** of the plot, or action. Since one purpose of the report is to tell the readers something about the book or film, the summary should be as complete and accurate as possible. It should not be very long, though. A summary **condenses** the original book or film. It takes out most of the detail and leaves only what is absolutely necessary to understand the story.

Before you can write a summary, you need to be sure that you know what the main ideas of the book or film are. The following activity will give you some practice in identifying the main idea.

Try It

Here are three paragraphs from a book about a Cherokee Indian. Following each paragraph are three sentences. Check the sentence that best expresses the main idea of the paragraph.

1. At the start, the Cherokees had felt nothing but friendship for the newcomers from across the water. They had greeted the white people as equals. It had never occurred to them to be suspicious of the motives of these new arrivals. They never thought that their new friends might betray them or that their land might be stolen from them. The Cherokees trusted these strangers as they would one of their own people.

_____ a. War between the Cherokees and the white people could not be avoided because the white people stole the Cherokees' land.

_____ b. The Cherokees accepted the white people at the start because they never suspected that the newcomers might not be trustworthy.

_____ c. The Cherokees and the white people always trusted each other, and their relationship was happy and peaceful.

2. The white settlers began to take advantage of the Cherokees, tricking them into giving up their land. The Indians became angry and bitter at this betrayal. Their land was disappearing, and they had no place to live. More and more Cherokees were forced to gather their belongings together and head westward.

_____ a. The Cherokees were forced to go West when the white settlers tricked them out of their land.

_____ b. The white settlers headed westward, looking for land to take over.

_____ c. The Cherokees sold all their land to the white settlers and used the money to go West.

---

continued . . .

3. The Indian tribes along the East Coast had failed to see that the real threat to them was the white settlers. They fought among themselves instead of joining together to fight the European invasion. Weakened by these battles, the Cherokees were unable to resist the white settlers. The newcomers were not content with just one piece of land. Soon they had pushed all the Cherokees off their land.

_____ a. All the Cherokees were killed off in wars with other Indian tribes, and the white settlers took over their land.

_____ b. The Europeans prevented the Indian tribes from banding together to defend their land.

_____ c. The mistake the Cherokees made was fighting other Indian tribes and not resisting the white settlers.

Once you know what the main ideas are, you need to be able to express them in your own words. The following activity will help you substitute your own words for the words in the original piece of writing.

Try It

Find each sentence you chose as a main idea in the activity before this one. Rewrite it in the space below, using your own words in the place of the original.

Example: Journeying westward to Oklahoma, the Cherokees suffered cold, starvation, and even death.

The Cherokees suffered terrible hardships
on the way to Oklahoma.

1. _____

_____

2. _____

_____

3. _____

_____

Now that you can find the main idea of a paragraph and express it in your own words, you are ready to write a summary. Keep in mind that a summary

- is shorter than the original
- contains just the main ideas and the most important details
- combines ideas
- does not add anything new
- does not contain your own opinions, even though it is written in your own words

Compare the summary below with the original paragraphs. Notice what is left out and what the difference in length is between the two passages.

Original

A female fox is fussy about her living quarters. Well before she gives birth to her young, she begins to check out the available dens in her territory. She cleans out each one, looking it over carefully to see if it will meet her needs. When she finally finds a den she likes, she often uses it over and over again, returning to it each year when she is ready to give birth. After she dies, the den may even become the property of one of her children, who will also return to it year after year.

It is no wonder that the ideal den is such a prize. It is usually in a forest for greater protection, but not far from an open area like a meadow so that the fox family can relax and play in the sun. It must also be near a convenient supply of water. The den is usually set into a hillside to give the fox a good lookout, and it has a number of entrances to make it easier to escape from enemies. Even the kind of soil matters. The female fox prefers her den to be in sandy soil that she can dig in easily.

Summary

A female fox chooses her den carefully. Her needs range from the den's location to the kind of soil it is in. She must be near water and have maximum protection from enemies. When she finds a den that meets all her requirements, she uses it for many years.

Try It

Reread the three paragraphs about the Cherokees. Make sure you know what the main ideas are. Decide what ideas can be combined and what ideas can be left out altogether. Then write a summary in your own words. Your summary should be about 4-5 sentences long.

_____

_____

_____

_____

_____

_____

_____

_____

PRACTICING THE PROCESS

Mario's Report

Mario looked through *Star Ka'at* again and picked out the main ideas. Then he wrote a summary of the plot, telling what happened in the book as briefly as possible. Here is Mario's plot summary.

Two Ka'ats named Tiro and Mer, who belong to a race of cats from another planet, come to Earth to rescue their kin. They make friends with two humans—a boy named Jim and a girl named Elly—who can read their thoughts. Both Elly and Jim have lost their parents and feel alone in the world, except for each other and for Tiro and Mer. Earth is in danger of being destroyed by the people who live on it. When it looks as though a war might break out and Elly and Jim will be separated from the Ka'ats and from each other, Tiro and Mer decide to take the two humans with them. They claim Elly and Jim as kin, and together they all leave Earth on the Ka'ats' spaceship.

Your Report WP

Review the plot of the book or film you decided to write about in the last lesson. Then pretend that you have one minute on a long-distance telephone call to tell a friend about the book or film you have chosen. Or pretend that you have to fit the main points onto a postcard you are writing to a friend. Write the main points you would select on the lines below.

_____

_____

_____

_____

_____

_____

_____

Now use these main points to write a summary of the plot of the book or film you are reporting on. Include only the most important supporting details, and combine ideas as much as possible. Your summary should contain 6-7 sentences.

_____

_____

_____

_____

_____

_____

_____

_____

_____

_____

Writing a Book or Film Report

A book or film report tells the readers enough so that they can decide whether they want to read the book or see the film.

WARMUP

When you write a report, the outline is part of the prewriting process. It helps you decide what you're going to say and how you're going to organize your facts and ideas. To write the first draft of the report, you need to turn the points on the outline into sentences and paragraphs.

Each main point of the outline (indicated by a Roman numeral) usually becomes the main idea of a paragraph. The supporting details (indicated by letters) are the sentences in the paragraph.

I. Kinds of buildings

   A. Apartment buildings

   B. Stores

   C. Post office

For example, the first paragraph of a report on your neighborhood could be written from the outline in this way.

My neighborhood has buildings of every size and shape. The apartment buildings tower over the others. Some are more than thirty stories high. Beneath them, on the street level, are the stores. You can buy almost anything in this one block—from a quart of milk to the newest records. At the end of the street, the post office, with its broad front steps and its flags, gives the whole neighborhood an official look.

Try It

Here is the second part of the outline for the report on your neighborhood:

II. Kinds of people

   A. Families with children

   B. Older people

Turn this outline into a paragraph about the neighborhood you live in. Write one introductory sentence that states the main idea. Then write one or two sentences for each of the supporting points.

_____

_____

_____

_____

---

continued . . .

_____

_____

_____

_____

_____

_____

PRACTICING THE PROCESS

Mario's Report

Mario's teacher reminded the class that a book or film report is organized in a special way. The opening paragraph introduces the book or film; the middle paragraph summarizes it; and the closing paragraph tells what you think of it and why. This organization is shown in the outline Mario wrote:

I. Introduction

   A. Title

   B. Author

   C. Theme

II. Summary

   A. Main characters

   B. Action

III. Conclusion

   A. My opinion

   B. Reasons

When he turned his outline into a report, Mario needed to state the theme of the book he had read. He knew that the theme gave the main idea of the book in one or two sentences, but he wasn't sure what those sentences should say. Then he remembered that TV programs often describe shows in one or two sentences:

A young boy and his grandfather learn from each other as they travel across the country together.

or

Jamie's parents decide to go on strike, with hilarious results as Jamie tries to manage the household himself.

Using this technique, Mario wrote a sentence stating the theme of _Star Ka'at_:

Two children make contact with representatives of a superior race of cats who have a special mission on Earth.

Your Report WP

Pretend your book or film is a television show, and you are describing it for the weekly television guide. On the lines below, state the theme of your book or film in one or two sentences.

_____

_____

_____

Mario's Report

Using the outline, the statement of the theme, and the plot summary he had already prepared, Mario wrote the first draft of his book report. Each main point of the outline became a paragraph. The statement of the theme became part of the first paragraph. The plot summary was the entire second paragraph. The third paragraph contained his opinion of the book, with reasons to support it.

Mario waited a day and then revised his report. He changed some words, took out part of one sentence, and added another sentence so that the report would say exactly what he wanted it to. After revising, he proofread and edited the report, checking spelling, punctuation, capitalization, and usage, and making sure that he had followed the correct form for his final copy.

When it had been revised, edited, and copied over, Mario's report looked like this:

Mario Nunez
Language Arts
March 28, 1986

Book Report on Star Ka'at

The book Star Ka'at is a science fiction novel by André Norton and Dorothy Madlee. It has illustrations by Bernard Colonna. It is about two children who make contact with space creatures on a special mission to Earth.

Two Ka'ats named Tiro and Mer, who belong to a race of cats from another planet, come to Earth to rescue their kin. They make friends with two humans—a boy named Jim and a girl named Elly—who can read their thoughts. Both Elly and Jim have lost their parents and feel alone in the world, except for each other and for Tiro and Mer. Earth is in danger of being destroyed by the people who live on it. When it looks as though a war might break out and Elly and Jim will be separated from the Ka'ats and from each other, Tiro and Mer decide to take the two humans with them. They claim Elly and Jim as kin, and together they all leave Earth on the Ka'ats' spaceship.

I enjoyed Star Ka'at very much. It is realistic about the world and shows many things that are wrong with modern life. At the same time, it shows hope for the future if people can learn to overlook differences between races the way Elly and Jim do. I would recommend it for anyone who likes science fiction or animal stories.

Your Report WP

On a separate sheet of paper, write the first draft of your book or film report. Remember to include the statement of the theme and the plot summary you have already written. Use the outline on page 93 to guide you.

Revise your report by crossing out, inserting, or changing whatever is needed. Then read it once again for spelling, punctuation, capitalization, and usage, and make all the necessary editing changes. When your report has been revised and edited, copy it over on another sheet of paper. Follow the form Mario used.

1. Put a heading in the upper right-hand corner of your paper. It should contain

   - your name

   - your class

   - the date

2. Put the title of the report on a separate line, in the center of the page. Follow the rules for capitalizing titles. Leave an extra line above and below the title.

3. Leave a margin at the top and bottom of each page and on the left and right.

4. Indent each paragraph five spaces or five letters.

WRITING PROJECTS: LETTERS

Many kinds of letters are really forms of description. When you tell someone how you've spent your vacation or how you've used the gift money you were sent, you are describing something. You are also describing something when you write to tell an employer something about yourself.

In this section you will practice writing two kinds of letters—a letter to a friend or a relative and a letter to an employer. You will learn what you need to know about the form of both kinds of letters, and again you will find out that the **process** of writing is the same for a letter as it is for a paragraph or a report.

Friendly Letters

Interesting letters have lots of details.

WARMUP

When you write more than one paragraph, you need a **transition**—a way of getting from one paragraph to the next. You can do this by

- telling your reader that something is coming
- making reference to something that has already been said

Here is an example of each kind of transition.

Method 1: Something is coming.

> I suppose you're wondering what took me so long to answer your last letter? Let me tell you, getting ready for a class trip takes even longer than going on the trip itself. One weekend in Washington, D.C., took more than three weeks of preparation.

(The next paragraph will obviously be about the weeks of preparation.)

Method 2: Referring to something that has already been said.

> Julie told us about her date for the dance at Sunday dinner two months before graduation. From that moment until she stepped out the door on Luis' arm, the whole house was in an uproar. It began with the dress. Mom, Julie, and Aunt Seretha didn't like any of the ones we could afford, so they decided to make one.

> First, they had to agree on a color.

(The rest of the paragraph is about making the dress.)

Try It

1. This paragraph is part of a letter Sam wrote to his Aunt Judy to thank her for the birthday money she sent him. He bought three things with the money. Add a final sentence to this paragraph that will connect it to a paragraph that follows it.

> Thanks so much for the check you sent me. I had a great birthday party and got a lot of presents and then your check came. It made my birthday last a lot longer. Last week I thought and thought about what I would buy with the money. _____

_____

_____

2. Sam's sister Rachel wrote her best friend a letter from Washington, D.C. Rachel thought that the most interesting part of her trip was the visit to the White House. Write the first sentence of the paragraph that follows this one.

---

continued . . .

After all the preparation, the trip was really worth it. I only wish we had had three weeks instead of three days to spend there. I liked everything I saw—the Zoo, the Smithsonian Museum, the cherry trees, the visit to our senator, the Library of Congress. I could go on and on, but I want to tell you about the part I liked best.

_____

_____

PRACTICING THE PROCESS

Carmelo's Letter

When T.J. received this letter from his friend Carmelo, he didn't write a reply—he telephoned to get more details.

Dear T.J.,

Thanks for your letter. Nothing much is happening except that I broke my arm in a bike race last week. That's why Jonelle is writing this letter for me. (She's my new girl friend.) I put the trophy in my room— on the dresser. See you in two weeks. Write soon.

Your friend,

Carmelo

Carmelo could have saved T.J. time and money if he had written at least one paragraph about the bike race and one about his new girl friend. If he had written a letter like the one below, T. J. would have enjoyed it much more. Notice how Carmelo joins the first and second paragraphs in this new letter.

October 16, 1989 ◁ DATE

GREETING ▷ Dear T.J.,

Thanks for sending me a copy of the article about bike racing. You know how much I like to ◁ BODY read about my favorite sport. It may not be my

105

favorite sport much longer, though. If you haven't guessed by now that I'm not writing this letter, take another look. Last week I won a great race but took a spill at the end and broke my arm. At least I get to look at the trophy as well as the cast. I also get to look at Jonelle, who's writing this letter for me.

Jonelle was helping her mother, who was the doctor in the medical tent at the race. When I got hurt, Jonelle brought me water and things and then she came to visit me at home. She's been visiting me every day, bringing me my homework and reading aloud to me when I get tired. It was almost worth a broken arm to meet her. Write soon.

Your friend, <——CLOSING

Carmelo <——SIGNATURE

Your Letter

Write a letter to a friend or a relative who doesn't live near you. You may thank the friend or relative for a gift, or you may tell about an experience you have had. Make your letter at least two paragraphs long and use either Method 1 or Method 2 to connect the paragraphs.

1. Use today's date.

2. Copy the form that Carmelo used. Pay attention to the punctuation and the spacing.

3. When you have written the first draft, read it over carefully and ask yourself if the letter says everything you want it to say. Make whatever changes you want, then edit the letter for capitalization, spelling and punctuation. Write a final copy on a separate sheet of paper.

continued...

Business Letters

When you apply for a job, describe what you can do.

WARMUP

José saw this announcement posted on the bulletin board at the school guidance office.

JOB OPENING

Do you like to work with children? If so, we may have a job for you. The Town of Packwood needs junior counsellors for the town playgrounds this summer. You should be between the ages of 12-16 and have an interest in one or more of the following:

sports	dance
art	drama
reading	cooking
crafts	music

Any experience—baby-sitting for others or for your own family—is a plus. Write a letter telling us what skills you have, and we'll arrange an interview. Send the letter to:

Ms. Celia Jackson
Director, Summer Counsellor Program
149 Eastwood Street
Packwood, Oregon 97478

The guidance counsellor gave José an *inventory* form to fill to help him write the letter. When storekeepers take inventory, they list all the things they have in the store that are worth something. When you fill out a personal inventory, you can list all the skills, experiences, and interests you have that will help you get a job.

PERSONAL INVENTORY

Name: José Soto

Age: 14

Skills:

Sports: soccer, baseball, running

Art: good at lettering signs

Reading: read aloud to my younger sister and to my grandmother

Crafts: make birdhouses and mailboxes out of wood

Dance: enjoy school dances

continued...

Drama: worked on the sets for class play

Cooking: make Sunday breakfasts: pancakes, eggs, French toast

Music: have a good record collection

Experience: take care of younger sister every day, babysit for older sister's two children on Friday nights

Try It

You are going to apply for a summer job too. Fill out the personal inventory before you write the letter.

PERSONAL INVENTORY

Name: _____

Age: _____

Skills: _____

    Sports: _____

    Art: _____

    Reading: _____

    Crafts: _____

    Dance: _____

    Drama: _____

    Cooking: _____

    Music: _____

    Experience: _____

PRACTICING THE PROCESS

José's Letter

José continued the prewriting process by thinking about what his letter should contain. He wrote this paragraph outline.

Paragraph 1: Tell what the letter is about.
Possible opening: I want to apply for the job you announced.

Paragraph 2: Describe my qualifications. Put the skills I'm best at first. Possible first sentence: I'm interested in all the things you mentioned, and would like to help other kids learn them.

Paragraph 3: Ask for interview - Tell when I'm available.

José wrote a rough draft on a word processor, showed it to the guidance counsellor, then revised and edited the letter. In the process, he changed the opening sentences of his paragraphs. When he made the final copy, he made sure that the letter was written in correct business style.

```
                                      49 Wooster Street          ◁ HEADING
                                      Packwood, Oregon 97476
                                      May 27, 1989

         Ms. Celia Jackson
         Director, Summer Counsellor Program   ◁ INSIDE ADDRESS
         149 Eastwood Street
         Packwood, Oregon 97476


         Dear Ms. Jackson:    ◁ GREETING

         I would like to apply for the job of junior counsellor for the town
         playgrounds this summer.  I am 14 years old and like to work with children.  ◁ BODY
         For two years now I have been baby-sitting my younger sister every day after
         school and on Friday nights I baby-sit with my niece and nephew.

         Although I'm interested in all the skills you listed, I'm particularly good at
         building things.  I've made sets for the school play and wooden birdhouses and
         mailboxes for the Crafts Fair. I could teach the children how to make them,
         and it wouldn't cost much money.  I've also been reading aloud to my sister
         every day for a year now and she really likes it.  I take her and my niece and
         nephew to the library to get reading books for the week.  I could take groups
         of children to the library to pick books for reading time at the playground.

         I hope this letter gives an idea of what I can do for the children.  Please
         let me know if you want me to come in for an interview.  I can be reached at
         746-7823 after school.


                                      Sincerely,     ◁ CLOSING

                                      José Flores   ◁ SIGNATURE
```

Your Letter WP

Using the personal inventory you made, write a letter answering this job announcement.

JOB OPENING

Announcing a special opportunity for the right student. Be a Summer School Helper! This year our town has planned an extra summer session that combines school subjects with sports, crafts, and a host of other activities. We need junior counsellors who can help elementary school children learn more fun things to do. If you are above the age of 12 and like children, one of these jobs could be yours. Tell us what you know about the following:

sports	dance
art	drama
reading	cooking
crafts	music

Baby-sitting experience a plus.
Send the letter to:

Ms. Shirley Conrad
Director, Summerfun
347 Buena Vista Avenue
Yourtown, Your State, Your ZIP

1. Use the name of your town and state and your own ZIP code in the Heading. Use today's date.

2. Copy the form that José used. Note that all the lines line up on the left in **block** form and that a colon (:) is used after the greeting. Pay attention to the spacing, too.

3. Remember that a good job application letter describes what it is about you that makes you good for the job.

4. When you have finished writing the first draft, ask yourself if the letter says everything you want it to say. Make whatever changes you feel are necessary, then edit the letter for capitalization, punctuation, and spelling. Write the final copy on a separate sheet of paper.

_____

_____

_____

_____

_____

_____

_____

_____

_____

continued . . .

Congratulations!
You have finished the book—and you have begun to be a real writer.